W9-DJJ-687

WITHDRAWN

Plant Propagation Lab Manual

Third Edition

Thomas A. Fretz
Paul E. Read
Mary C. Peele

Illustrated by Barbara W. Ellis

The Ohio State University
Columbus, Ohio
and
The University of Minnesota
St. Paul, Minnesota

 **Burgess Publishing Company**
Minneapolis, Minnesota

Contents

FOREWORD v

INTERMITTENT MIST PROPAGATION √ 1
 LABORATORY PROJECT I. Mist Propagation - Cost Project. 17

PROPAGATION MEDIA 23
 LABORATORY PROJECT II. Physical Properties of Some Media. 29
 LABORATORY PROJECT III. Evaluation of Types of Rooting Media. 35
 LABORATORY PROJECT IV. A Demonstration of the Principle of
  Aeration on Root Production. 43

ASEXUAL PROPAGATION OF CUTTINGS 49
 LABORATORY PROJECT V. Type of Cuttings. 59
 LABORATORY PROJECT VI. Influence of Leaf Area on Root Development. 63
 LABORATORY PROJECT VII. Evaluation of Methods for the Reduction
  of Water Loss from Leafy Cuttings. 69
 LABORATORY PROJECT VIII. Maintenance of Healthy Planting and
  Rooting Stock (Culture-Indexing). 77

JUVENILITY 81
 LABORATORY PROJECT IX. Influence of Tissue Age on the Rooting
  of Cuttings. 85
 LABORATORY PROJECT X. Evaluation of the Size of Cuttings and
  the Type of Wood. 91

GROWTH REGULATORS √ 97
 LABORATORY PROJECT XI. Evaluation of Growth Regulator Concen-
  tration on Root Initiation. 101
 LABORATORY PROJECT XII. Evaluation of the Duration of Growth
  Regulator Application on Root Initiation. 109
 LABORATORY PROJECT XIII. Rooting of Cuttings from Flowering and
  Vegetative Plants. 117
 LABORATORY PROJECT XIV. Evaluation of Apical, Medial and Basal
  Hardwood Cuttings. 125
 LABORATORY PROJECT XV. Wounding Cuttings. 133
 LABORATORY PROJECT XVI. Evaluation of the Influence of Polarity
  on Root Development of Cuttings. 141
 LABORATORY PROJECT XVII. Preparation of Root Cuttings. 147

FERNS 151
 LABORATORY PROJECT XVIII. Propagation of Ferns by Spores. 155

GRAFTING   159
    LABORATORY PROJECT XIX.   Whip and Tongue Grafting.   171
    LABORATORY PROJECT XX.   Cleft Grafting.   175

BUDDING   179
    LABORATORY PROJECT XXI.   T or Shield Budding.   185
    LABORATORY PROJECT XXII.   Chip Budding.   189

LAYERING   193
    LABORATORY PROJECT XXIII.   Air Layering.   201

SEED PROPAGATION   205
    LABORATORY PROJECT XXIV.   Preconditioning Woody Plant Seeds.   209
    LABORATORY PROJECT XXV.   Photoreversible Control of Seed Germin-
        ation.   221
    LABORATORY PROJECT XXVI.   Influence of Various Chemical Factors
        on Seed Germination.   227

SEED TESTING   233
    LABORATORY PROJECT XXVII.   Testing for Seed Viability and
        Germination.   235

SEED SOWING   241
    LABORATORY PROJECT XXVIII.   Seed Sowing.   245

PROPAGATION OF SPECIALIZED STEMS   249
    LABORATORY PROJECT XXIX.   Propagation of Specialized Stems.   255
    LABORATORY PROJECT XXX.   Production of Tubers from Leaf-Bud
        Cuttings.   259
    LABORATORY PROJECT XXXI.   Propagation of Lilies by Scaling.   263

PROPAGATION BY TISSUE CULTURE   267
    LABORATORY PROJECT XXXII.   Micropropagation of Chrysanthemum. 273
    LABORATORY PROJECT XXXIII.   Aseptic Micropropagation of Petunia. 277

APPENDIX I - GLOSSARY OF TERMS   283

APPENDIX II - ROOTING SELECTED WOODY ORNAMENTALS   291

APPENDIX III - PROPAGATING SELECTED HOUSE PLANTS   297

APPENDIX IV - WOODY PLANTS AND HERBACEOUS PERENNIAL GENERA THAT ARE
    CAPABLE OF BEING PROPAGATED BY ROOT CUTTINGS   301

APPENDIX V - LAYERING SELECTED WOODY ORNAMENTALS   303

APPENDIX VI - GUIDELINES FOR THE GERMINATION OF SOME ANNUAL, POT
    PLANT AND ORNAMENTAL HERB SEEDS   305

APPENDIX VII - GUIDELINES FOR THE GERMINATION OF VEGETABLE SEEDS   309

APPENDIX VIII - SCARIFICATION AND STRATIFICATION REQUIREMENTS FOR
    SELECTED WOODY ORNAMENTALS   311

Foreword

The <u>Plant Propagation Lab Manual</u> has been revised to facilitate its use as a supplement to a lecture-discussion course on plant propagation for horticulture students. This laboratory manual is so designed that it can be used in the traditional plant propagation laboratory or in an audiotutorial (self-study) laboratory, where it is possible for the student to complete the exercises independently. The manual can be used alone or as a companion to any of the available textbooks in plant propagation.

Several exercises are designed to give the student a better understanding of the intermittent mist system and its construction costs, the physical properties of propagation media, the role which juvenility plays in the rooting process, the effect of growth regulators on root initiation, whip and tongue grafting, T budding, air layering, the photo-reversible control of seed germination, the propagation of specialized stems, and tissue culture. Exercises are included which emphasize both the physiological processes which occur during propagation and the application of these practices. Thought Provokers are included at the conclusion of each laboratory project to help the student thoroughly understand the exercise.

In addition to the laboratory exercises, the manual contains in-depth discussions on intermittent mist propagation, propagation media, asexual propagation by cuttings, growth regulators, grafting and budding techniques, layering, seed propagation, propagation of specialized stem structures, and tissue culture. The appendices include a glossary of terms, along with guidelines for the propagation of woody ornamentals, house plants, vegetable crops, annuals, and perennials.

We wish to express our appreciation to Barbara Ellis, John Nagy, and Jacqueline Neumann for the skillful preparation of all the artwork and to Bonnie Szymanski, Pamela Staton, and Mildred Daniels for their many efforts in typing and retyping of the manuscript. In addition, we would like to give special thanks to Dr. Fenton E. Larsen, Department of Horticulture, Washington State University, Pullman, Washington, who kindly gave us permission to use Figure 37, which was reprinted from <u>Pacific Northwest Cooperative Extension Publication</u> 164. Special thanks are given to graduate students Barry Eisenberg, Larry Kuhns, Anne Boyne, Julia Martens, Mary Lewnes, Wendy Sheppard, Stephen Garton, Scott Walcker, and John Preece, who assisted not only in teaching laboratory sections of plant propagation, but who gave of valuable time and effort during the preparation, revision, and proofreading of materials over the past 5 years. Their encouragement and cooperation have stimulated this effort. We are most grateful to them all.

Intermittent Mist Propagation

Mist propagation facilities were introduced as an advance in the field of plant propagation about 1950. While the use of mist is not exactly new, experimental workers have been using automatically controlled mist in plant propagation since 1940. Historically, the practice of spraying water on the foliage of plants to reduce wilting, often referred to as syringing, is as old as horticulture itself.

The terms mist and automatic watering need clarification. While both terms are used synonymously, mist differs from automatic watering in that misting is actually the applying of a small amount of water at one time, while automatic watering implies the application of mist more or less continuously at regular intervals throughout the day. When the term is used today, "mist" implies intermittent use of mist through an automatic system.

When investigators first began to experiment with automatic mechanisms for water control, they were attempting humidity control. However, emphasis shifted to spraying water directly on plant foliage. Automatic devices for mist propagation have, as a result, made rooting of softwood and/or herbaceous cuttings a simple procedure.

When cuttings are removed from the parent plant they continue to transpire, or lose water through their leaves, like any intact plant. However, cuttings are poorly equipped to obtain water without an intact root system. In the past, methods used in the vegetative propagation of plants to increase humidity and subsequently reduce wilting during the rooting period have involved heavy shading, reducing leaf area, frequent hand watering and various types of enclosures. These practices, however, greatly reduced photosynthesis, thereby causing a slower rate of root initiation and development.

In recent years, the utilization of intermittent mist has resulted in increased successes with the rooting of cuttings, and consequently, has changed many of the older propagation practices. With intermittent mist, cuttings of many species can be rooted under high light intensities with little or no leaf scorch. This is due to the maintenance of high atmospheric relative humidity during the rooting period. In addition, intermittent mist provides a cooling effect as water is evaporated from the leaf surfaces of the cuttings. Thus with intermittent mist, transpiration is reduced, leaf tissues are cooled, respiration is reduced and photosynthesis continues, allowing for the increased production of carbohydrates necessary for rapid development of the root system.

Aside from the physiological benefits, mist has many other advantages. They can be easily divided into three classes: a) cultural, b) labor saving, and c) economic.

Culturally, the mist system enables the propagator to take larger leafy cuttings that provide larger, stronger, healthier plants when rooted. In addition, softwood cuttings of many plants can be taken earlier in the growing season. This succulent material is fast growing and has active cambium tissue present which increases the chances of rooting. Mist also provides an extension of the propagating season for most plants.

Mist is advantageous to the propagator in other ways. Without the need for shading, no labor is required to apply and remove shading materials from greenhouse glass. Nutrients also can be added to the mist, thus reducing the need for manual fertilizing of plants. Probably most evident among the advantages is that mist eliminates the need for the constant syringing and watering that previously were standard propagation practices.

Lastly, the intermittent mist system can be an economic asset to the propagator. Experimental work has shown that not only do a greater percentage of cuttings root, but rooting occurs at a faster rate when using an intermittent mist system. This is important in that there is a faster turnover of cuttings, thus making greater economic use of propagating space.

The mist may have some drawbacks. One such drawback is that misting leaches nutrient elements from the leaves. However, misting with the incorporation of nutrients, often termed "nutrient mist", replenishes the leached elements.

Mist must also be used properly to obtain the best results. Proper amounts of water with provision for good drainage must be used to prevent waterlogging and excessive cooling of the rooting medium. In addition, cuttings must be taken during the proper season. These are all factors that can be regulated by the propagator and they must be adjusted properly or diastrous results may occur.

A schematic diagram illustrating the component parts of an intermittent mist system is shown in Figure 1. Various systems with and without environmental overrides give the propagator several alternatives to best meet his needs.

TYPES OF MIST
    In general, misting techniques may be classified into two types, continuous and intermittent. With continuous mist, a fine spray of water is applied continuously to the cuttings during the rooting period. Continuous misting may lower the temperature of the rooting medium below the optimum for rooting and cause excessive leaching and deterioration of the foliage. In addition, if drainage is poor, the excess water used in the constant mist system may displace oxygen in the medium, resulting in poor root development and decay of stem tissue.

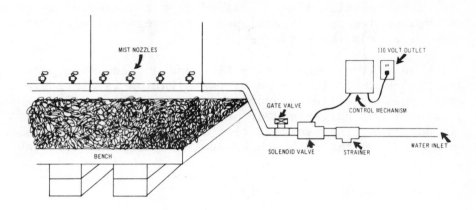

FIGURE 1. SCHEMATIC DIAGRAM OF THE OVERALL MIST SYSTEM.

Controlled intermittent mist (i.e., mist "on" for a period of time and "off" usually for a longer period) reduces the amount of water used when compared to continuous mist and can prevent the waterlogged soil condition that often results with the use of constant mist.

With intermittent mist systems a control mechanism and solenoid valve are required. The control mechanisms may be of various types, including timing devices, humidistats, light operated devices and electronically controlled units.

INTERMITTENT MIST INSTALLATION

Construction and design of the propagation bench will vary with the needs of the propagator. For intermittent mist propagation, 2 types of benches can be constructed, the ground bed and the raised bench. Ground beds (Figure 2) are most commonly employed where intermittent mist propagation is done in outside conditions, while raised propagation benches are most commonly used in greenhouse or plastic-covered structures.

Regardless of the type of bench, size will depend upon the needs of the propagator. Length of both ground or raised benches will vary, depending on the facilities and particular needs of the propagator. Both raised and ground beds should not exceed 1.5 m (60 in) in width, so the center can be easily reached from both sides of the bench. With raised benches, height varies from 0.75-0.90 m (30 to 36 in), depending upon the type of construction.

Once the type of bed has been decided, there are 2 types of installation for the intermittent mist lines - overhead and in-bench. For ground beds, in-bench mist lines are most commonly employed, as there is usually no means of support for overhead mist lines. Raised beds constructed in greenhouses or fiberglass houses are usually equipped with overbench mist lines attached or strung with wire from the crossties.

With overhead systems, the supply line and nozzles hang over the center of the propagation bench. This type of installation is particularly useful with the newer types of deflection nozzles which are installed by drilling and tapping into either galvanized or polyethylene pipe, so no "T's" are required. In addition, the overhead mist system is generally easier to install and maintain than the in-bench system, as all parts are readily accessible.

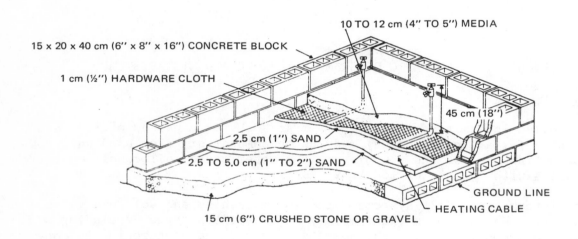

FIGURE 2. CUTAWAY VIEW SHOWING CONSTRUCTION OF A GROUND BED FOR OUTDOOR PROPAGATION. WIDTH OF BED SHOWN IS 1.5 M (60 IN). NOZZLES ARE SPACED 75 CM (30 IN) APART AND 38 CM (15 IN) FROM SIDE AND END OF BED.

The main disadvantage of the overhead mist system is that it is very susceptible to wind if used in the outdoor situation, making it imperative to use a wind screen in order to protect the cuttings and insure complete mist coverage.

With in-bench mist installation, the supply pipe runs along the bottom of the bed or bench either under the rooting medium or on the surface of the medium. The nozzles are placed on upright pipes attached to the supply line with "T's". In general, the nozzles in the in-bench type mist systems are 35 to 45 cm (14 to 18 in) above the medium. When permanently installing the in-bench mist system, the supply line should be placed under the medium so it will not take up space which can be used for propagation. Placing the mist line on top of the medium is useful when the propagator wishes to leave the cuttings in the medium but wants to move the mist line to another bench.

When using the ground bed in the outside situation, a polyethylene or burlap wind screen 0.6 to 0.9 m (2 to 3 ft) high should be constructed around the propagation bench to eliminate the problem of wind drift.

STRAINERS
The inclusion of a line strainer in the mist system is an integral part of the total system and is one of the most inexpensive items which can be used to help insure long solenoid and mist nozzle life. The major purpose of the strainer is to filter water prior to its passing through the solenoid, thereby preventing damage to the valve. In addition, the line strainer also helps to reduce the chances of clogging occurring in the mist nozzles.

The most common strainer used is the "Y" type which includes an 80 to 100 mesh screen basket. The basket can be cleaned periodically. In addition, straight-flow and "T" type strainers are available with removable screens for maintenance. Price of strainers varies depending upon size, type and source of supply.

SOLENOID VALVES
In any propagation system involving the use of intermittent mist, a solenoid valve is essential (Figure 3). Basically, the solenoid is an electrically operated valve used to control the flow of water through the misting system. Solenoid valves are available in 2 types, the "normally-open" valve and the "normally-closed" modes (Figure 4).

The normally-open solenoid is constructed to allow water to pass through the valve when the electric current is "off". When electric current is applied to the normally-open solenoid the valve closes, shutting off the flow of water. The normally-open solenoid offers the greatest possible pro-tection to the propagator in the case of power failure. In this type of situation, the mist would run continuously and protect all cuttings from dessication. Where the normally-open solenoid is used, it is often recom-mended that a gate valve be placed in the same line to act as a manual off-on valve if power failures occur (Figure 4).

FIGURE 3.   SOLENOID VALVE.

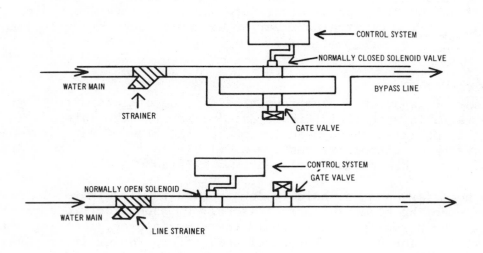

FIGURE 4.   SCHEMATIC DESIGN OF MIST SYSTEMS UTILIZING
NORMALLY-CLOSED AND NORMALLY-OPEN SOLENOID VALVE.

The normally-closed solenoid is the more common unit and is often less expensive at the time of the initial purchase than the normally-open type. The normally-closed solenoid is open only when the current is turned "on" by some type of control device. This type of solenoid will operate as efficiently as the normally-open solenoid, but has the disadvantage of remaining closed when the electric current is "off". When using this type of solenoid, it is recommended that a bypass be built into the system so that in times of power failure the mist can be manually operated (Figure 4).

Solenoids vary in cost, depending upon the source, type (either normally-open or normally-closed) and size of the valve.

In addition, it is often a good practice to include a 24 volt transformer along with a solenoid valve to reduce the line current from the normal 120 volts. As a solenoid is often close to wet, moist working conditions, this is often a rather inexpensive safety item to include.

MIST NOZZLES
Basically, there are two types of mist nozzles available for plant propagation: (1) Oil burner types (Figure 5) and (2) Deflection types (Figure 6).

FIGURE 5. OIL BURNER NOZZLE.

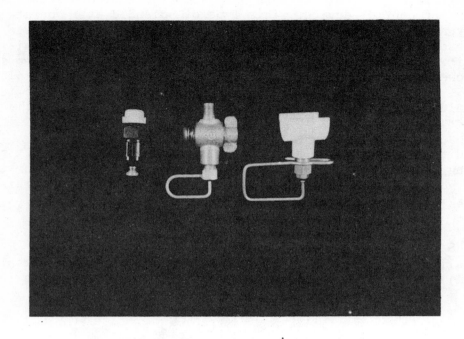

FIGURE 6. DEFLECTION NOZZLES (LEFT TO RIGHT). FLORA-MIST
FOGGER NO. 300 WITH FLORA-MIST PIPE SADDLE;
JED-MIST NOZZLE WITH JED-MIST PETCOCK; EDDY-
MIST NOZZLE.

The oil burner nozzle is still used in plant propagation, but not to the extent it once was due to its high initial cost. This type of nozzle produces a finely distributed spray, achieved by passing a stream of water through small grooves set at angles to each other. While the major advantage of the oil burner type nozzle is its use of only small volumes of water (2.5 to 5 gallons per hour), it requires water pressures of 50-100 lb/sq in to operate satisfactorily. In addition, oil burner nozzles cover a relatively small area per nozzle (0.3 to 0.4 sq m or 3.3 to 4 sq ft), thus requiring a greater number of nozzles per given area of bench space to achieve adequate coverage. Another disadvantage of the oil burner nozzle is the frequency with which it becomes clogged.

The deflection nozzle is by far the most commonly used by plant propagators. It produces a rather coarse spray as a result of a stream of water striking a flat surface, thereby producing the mist. While the large opening reduces the chances of clogging, the volume of water used is greater, varying from 4 to 20 gallons per hour. In general, the deflection nozzle covers a greater area, so a smaller number of nozzles can be used in design of the mist bench. An additional advantage of the deflection nozzle is that it will operate with water pressures as low as 20 pounds per square inch.

Specific characteristics including area of coverage, optimum operating pressure, hourly rate of discharge and additional comments concerning the more commonly available mist nozzles used in intermittent mist systems are listed in Table 1.

TABLE 1. CHARACTERISTICS OF SOME COMMONLY USED NOZZLES FOR INTERMITTENT MIST SYSTEMS.

Description	Type	Area of Coverage	Operating Pressure	Rate of Discharge	Comments
		(sq m)	(lb/sq in)	(gal/hr)	
Flora-Mist Fogger	Deflection	.55-.65	40	4-14	1/32" orifice 1/8" std pipe threads
Mist-er Green Fogger	Deflection	.46-.65	20	12	.040" orifice
			40	17	5/16-24 machine threads
			60	20	
Fog-Mist Nozzle #550	Deflection	.37	20	6	3/8" std pipe threads
Fog-Mist Nozzle #551	Deflection	.37	20	6	1/8" std pipe threads
Jed-Mist Nozzle	Deflection	.37	40	1	5/16-24 machine threads
Eddy-Mist Nozzles	Deflection	1.11	45	90	Requires adaptor
Supreme Electric A6	Oil Burner	.28-.37	100	15	1/2" pipe fitting
Supreme Electric T16	Oil Burner	1.39	50	1.5	

MIST CONTROLLING DEVICES

Selection of intermittent controlling systems presents some problems to the propagator, as several different types of systems are commercially available. Intermittent mist propagation systems can be constructed in one of two modes:

(1) Preset system.
(2) Variable system, completely dependent upon the environment.

Although both types of systems have been used successfully by plant propagators, the variable system which is completely dependent upon the environment is the most sensitive and is the most highly recommended system.

PRESET SYSTEMS

Environmental conditions have no influence on the misting frequency or duration of the mist when time clocks or humidistats are used to control the intermittent misting system. Keen observation of the cuttings and the medium, followed by manual adjustment daily, may be needed when operating without environmentally controlled devices. Prolonged periods with or without sunshine can markedly affect clock adjustments (Table 2).

TABLE 2. TYPES OF INTERMITTENT MIST PROPAGATION SYSTEMS AND CONTROL EQUIP-
MENT REQUIRED.

Mode of Operation	Control System	Equipment Required
Preset-System	Time	24-hour time clock, interval timer, and solenoid valve
	Humidity	Humidistat and solenoid
Environmental Cycle	Evaporation	Plastic leaf (2 electrodes in non-conducting substance), electronic relay circuit and solenoid valve
	Weight	Balance, mercury switch, relays and solenoid valve
	Light	Photocell, electronic control unit and solenoid valve

1. TIME CLOCK CONTROLS

By far, the most popular intermittent mist system with propagators are time clock controls regulating a solenoid valve. With this type of preset system, two time-clocks are required. The day-night or 24 hour timer is used to turn the system "on" in the morning and "off" in the evening at predetermined times, depending on the material being propagated. In addition to the day-night timer, a cycle timer is wired to the solenoid valve to regulate the mist cycle during the hours the day-night timer is "on". Cycle timers for this regulation system are available in several forms, including the 1 minute maximum cycle with 1 second on-off intervals, 6 minute maximum cycles with 6 second on-off cycles and 12 minute maximum cycles with 12 seconds on-off cycles (Figure 7).

The time clock system must be set to keep cuttings covered with moisture under the most rapid drying conditions. As a result, numerous manual adjustments are required during periods when the evaporation rate is low, i.e., early morning, late evening or cloudy days.

Since environmental conditions change during the rooting period, factors such as light, temperature and humidity also can be used to regulate the intermittent mist system.

2. HUMIDITY CONTROLS

A humidistat has been used in some instances to entirely replace the time clock system in regulating the time of the day during which the mist is applied. However, since drying of the leaves of cuttings is not directly proportional to the level of humidity, this type of control has not been used greatly among propagators.

10

FIGURE 7. TIME CLOCK CONTROLS USED FOR AUTOMATIC OPERATION
           OF AN INTERMITTENT MIST SYSTEM. THE 24-HOUR
           CLOCK (LEFT) TURNS THE SYSTEM "ON" IN MORNING AND
           "OFF" IN EVENING. THE 6-MINUTE INTERVAL TIMER
           (RIGHT) CONTROLS THE INTERVAL OF MIST. NOTE THE
           SINGLE TAB AT THE 4 MINUTE MARK, WHICH ALLOWS THE
           MIST TO COME "ON" FOR 6 SECONDS EVERY 6 MINUTES.

VARIABLE SYSTEMS COMPLETELY DEPENDENT UPON THE ENVIRONMENT
     With variable type systems there are no time clocks to regulate the
misting interval or duration. Rather, there are separate systems which depend upon evaporation, weight, or light to control the mist cycle.

     1. ELECTRONIC LEAF
     The electronic leaf is used in a variable misting system which operates
on the principle of evaporation in order to maintain a uniform level of humidity at the leaf surface. This system consists of two electrodes imbedded in
plastic or a similar nonconductive surface. The electrodes are wired to a
central control box which is connected to the solenoid valve.

     The electronic leaf operates on the principle that moisture will evapor-
ate from the plastic, nonconductive leaf at about the same rate as it does
from the leaf surface of the cuttings. When the moisture between the two
electrodes is evaporated and electric current is broken, the solenoid is
activated and the mist is turned on. When a film of water has re-established
itself between the two electrodes, the solenoid is deactivated by the control

11

unit and the mist is turned off (Figure 8).

Theoretically, the electronic leaf can maintain a film of water on the leaves of the cuttings at all times, thus automatically compensating for changes in the evaporative power of the atmosphere surrounding the leaf. This system, however, varies with the placement of the plastic leaf in the propagation bed. When using the electronic leaf system in outdoor propagation beds, it is difficult to properly locate the plastic leaf so that wind drift will not affect the amount of water applied.

In addition, water with a high content of mineral matter or salts will make the operation of the electronic leaf system difficult. Where these water conditions exist, it is common for salts to be deposited on the plastic leaf between the contact points, thus completing the circuit and preventing the water from coming on. To overcome this condition, disconnect the power source from the plastic leaf and remove the accumulated salt from the plastic with a knife blade. Follow this procedure periodically to insure proper working of the electronic leaf system.

FIGURE 8. MACPENNY ELECTRONIC LEAF.

2. WEIGHT SYSTEM (MIST-A-MATIC)

Another common system used to regulate the intermittent mist in a propagation bed is based on the weight of water. A small, stainless steel screen is attached to a lever which activates a mercury switch. When sufficient water collects on the screen, the screen is lowered. This activates the mercury switch which closes the solenoid, thus turning off the mist. As the water evaporates from the screen, the screen rises and closes the mercury switch, which opens the solenoid and turns on the mist (Figures 9 and 10).

While this system is advertised as being maintenance free, in reality it requires attention similar to that necessary with the electronic leaf. Where water is known to have a high level of salt, the stainless screen must be cleaned periodically to prevent a salt buildup. If neglected, this condition could hold the system permanently in the "on" position. The weight system is most commonly sold under the trade name of Mist-A-Matic (Figures 9 and 10).

FIGURE 9.   CONTROL UNIT FOR A MIST-A-MATIC SYSTEM FOR REGULATION OF THE INTERMITTENT MIST SYSTEM.   NOTE THE STAINLESS STEEL SCREEN (LEFT) WHICH ACTIVATES THE SYSTEM.

13

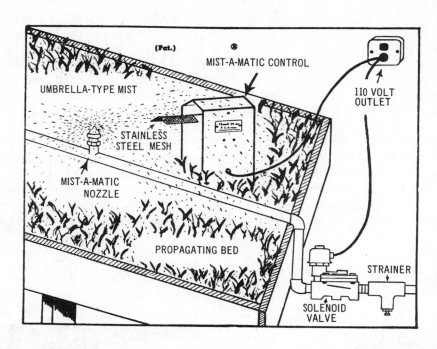

FIGURE 10. SCHEMATIC DIAGRAM OF THE MIST-A-MATIC SYSTEM. (COURTESY
OF E. C. GEIGER CO., HARLEYSVILLE, PA.)

3. SOLATROL

An environmentally dependent light operated system is known commercially
as the Solatrol. The Solatrol is used for propagation without 24-hour time
clocks or interval timers and operates strictly on light accumulation by the
photocell. This completely environmentally controlled system regulates the
misting cycle by activating the solenoid valve after a predetermined quantity
of foot-candles of light is absorbed by the photocell during a given period
of time. In addition, the duration of the mist cycle can be adjusted, depending upon the needs of the crop being propagated (Figure 11).

COSTS ASSOCIATED WITH INTERMITTENT MIST PROPAGATION FACILITIES

While much has been written about the principles, techniques and equipment required in intermittent mist propagation, little information is available, other than from various horticultural suppliers' catalogs, on the
prices associated with obtaining this type of equipment.

The cost of mist controlling systems will vary considerably depending
upon the type, source and quality of the equipment selected and the particular requirement of each propagator. There will be special cases where
booster pumps may be required to increase line pressure or special filters
may be necessary if the water supply has a large amount of particulate matter
present. Such special equipment would obviously increase the basic costs of
an intermittent mist system.

14

FIGURE 11.   SOLATROL SYSTEM FOR CONTROL OF THE
INTERMITTENT MIST SYSTEM.

SELECTED REFERENCE MATERIALS

Halfacre, R. G. and H. M. Ellis.   1972.   Intermittent mist propagation.   N.
Car. Agri. Ext. Ser. Cir. 506.

Hartmann, H. T. and D. E. Kester.   1975.   Plant propagation - principles and
practices - 3rd ed.   Prentice-Hall, Inc., Englewood Cliffs, N.J.

Pokorny, F. A.   1965.   An evaluation of various equipment and media used for
mist propagation and their relative costs.   Ga. Agri. Expt. Sta. Bull.
N.S. 139.

LABORATORY PROJECT I. MIST PROPAGATION - COST PROJECT.

As you know, one of the most important factors in the successful propagation of cuttings is the ability to provide a suitable environment through the use of a properly regulated intermittent mist system which allows for the maintenance of a high relative humidity during the rooting period. In addition, this intermittent mist provides a cooling effect as water is evaporated from the leaf surface of the cutting. Thus with the advent of the intermittent mist system, transpiration is reduced, leaf tissues are cooled, respiration is reduced and photosynthesis continues, allowing for the production of carbohydrates necessary for rapid development of the root system.

PURPOSE:
To design an intermittent mist system, and prepare an itemized cost analysis for the system and the medium required for the propagation bed.

CASE PROBLEM:
You have just completed your horticultural degree at Old Glory State University and upon being hired at Smith's Garden Center you have been requested to prepare an itemized cost analysis for the building of a new intermittent mist system. After looking over the situation, you note that a bench is available in the company's greenhouse and that the water line is located at the end of the bench. Given the following information, design and calculate the costs of the intermittent mist system based on the most recent catalogs of the major horticultural supply houses.

1. Given
   a) The existing bed is 23.8 m x 1.2 m (75 ft x 4 ft).
   b) The main water supply is located at the end of the bench.
   c) The propagation bed will require 4.2 cu m (150 cu ft) of a peat-perlite (1:1) medium.

2. Calculate
   a) Total cost of the delivery equipment (pipe, elbows, tees, unions, caps, etc.) needed, starting from the main water line.
   b) Total cost of the electrical equipment including the time clock system (day-night and cycle timer).
   c) Total cost of equipment and Mist-A-Matic type system.
   d) Total cost of the equipment and electronic leaf type system.
   e) Total cost of medium for the bed.

NOTES

18

NAME _____

LAB SECTION _____

MIST PROPAGATION
COST PROJECT
MIST SYSTEM

Trade Catalog	Item Order No.	Description	Price Per Unit	Quantity	Cost
2a (Equipment- pipe, unions, tees, etc.)					

Equipment Subtotal (2a) _____

2b (Time-Clock
   Controls)

Total (Time Clock System) (2b) _____

Equipment Subtotal (2a) _____

Total (Time Clock System + Equipment) (2a + 2b) _____

Trade Catalog	Item Order No.	Description	Price Per Unit	Quantity	Cost
2c (Mist-A-Matic)					

Total (Mist-A-Matic) (2c)

Equipment Subtotal (2a)

Total (Mist-A-Matic + Equipment) (2a + 2c)

2d (Electronic Leaf)					

Total (Electronic Leaf) (2d)

Equipment Subtotal (2a)

Total (Electronic Leaf + Equipment) (2a + 2d)

COST OF MEDIUM

2e (Medium)					

Total Cost of Medium

Cost Per Cu M

THOUGHT PROVOKERS

1. Now that you have completed this exercise in estimating the overall costs of an intermittent mist system, what control system would you select for your own nursery and/or greenhouse business? Be sure to clearly indicate along with your answer WHY you have made this choice!

2. What would you expect to be the benefits to overall plant growth and development as a result of using a properly regulated intermittent mist system during the propagation phase of your production cycle?

Propagation Media

Numerous materials in dozens of various combinations are available for the germination of seeds and the rooting of cuttings. In general, the following characteristics are considered essential for a good propagation medium.

1. The medium must have sufficient body or firmness in order to hold or support the cuttings and/or seeds in place during the rooting or germination process.
2. It must be capable of retaining sufficient moisture so that watering does not have to be too frequent. In addition, the medium must not shrink excessively after drying.
3. The medium must also be sufficiently porous or well-drained so excessive water drains away, thereby permitting adequate aeration.
4. In addition, the medium used for propagation should not be saline or contain toxic substances, should be capable of being sterilized, be disease and insect-free and provide an adequate environment for root growth once root initiation has taken place, and be able to be uniformly and economically reproduced.

Many mixtures have been used for the purpose of growing plants and vary from field soil to very sophisticated mixtures of organic and inorganic substances. Included among those materials which have been mentioned in the literature are sand of various types and particle sizes, peat, ashes, cinders, flu-dust or fly-ash, sawdust, pine, fir and hardwood bark, sphagnum moss, rice hulls, cocoa fiber, vermiculite, perlite, styrofoam, calcined clay (turface or kitty-litter), and processed wood fiber.

In order to be a successful propagator, one should have an understanding of soils and in particular propagation medium. For a medium to be useful in propagation it should meet certain characteristics; namely, being inexpensive and readily available. In addition, the material must be uniform, long-lasting, disease, insect and weed-free, easily managed so that it does not become water-logged and must be able to hold a rather uniform temperature.

While much work has related to the effects of various media on rooting, no research indicates that any medium has a direct effect on root initiation. This discussion should be prefaced with the statement that numerous investigators and commercial propagators have found variable success with rooting plants in different media, thus indicating that there is no "best medium" for all plants in all conditions. The variable results are due to plant type, condition of the cutting, season, light, temperature, drainage, means of providing water, type of structure, and growth regulator treatment. Although the medium does not have a direct influence on the root initiation, it may have a marked effect on root elongation, type of root system, plant survival, and success in transplanting.

As we proceed with the discussion of rooting media perhaps we should take time out to define soil. By definition, soil is a mixture of weathered particles of rock and decayed organic matter composed of solids, liquids and gases. Approximately one-half of the mass of soil is solid and the other half composed of liquids and air spaces. These must be in the proper proportions for proper growth to take place. With container-grown plant material about 20% air space is necessary in order for proper growth and development.

The solid portion of a soil includes both organic and inorganic fractions. The inorganic fraction is derived from weathered parent materials and is basically composed of mineral matter. The size of the inorganic fractions range from colloidal to that of large pea gravel with the texture determined by the various portions of particles of different sizes. These particles make up the framework of the solid portion of the soil, while the colloidal material is a storehouse for nutrients essential for growth.

The organic portion of the solid material in soil is composed of both living and dead organisms including bacteria, fungi, earthworms, plant roots, and animal remains in various stages of decay. The decayed plant and animal remains, sometimes termed "humus", are an additional source of colloidal material having large nutrient and water-holding capacities.

The second portion of soil is the liquid portion which is primarily composed of water, dissolved oxygen, CO_2 and nutrients, while the third portion of the soil system is essentially the gaseous phase of the soil solution. In poorly drained or water-logged soils, water replaces the air space or space for gases, allowing no oxygen for roots or survival of microorganisms.

While our discussion up to now has dealt with field soil, this material is not used in container production of nursery stock or in propagation unless amended with other ingredients.

Of all the materials which can be used in artificial media, one of the more common is sand. This material is generally composed of small rock grains ranging from 0.05 through 2.0 millimeters in diameter. Quartz sand is generally used for propagation and is mined and washed and has no chemical or biological activity. Sand contains no nutrients or buffer capacity and as its size increases, the size of the spaces between the soil particles increases, facilitating greater air and water movement.

The second material found in many propagation media is peat or moss-peat. Moss-peat is simply the remains of aquatic, marsh, bog or swamp vegetation which has been preserved under water in a partially decomposed state. Generally, peat is classified depending upon the botanical composition of the partially decayed material. Sphagnum moss comes from herbaceous acid bog plants of the genus Sphagnum, generally having a pH of 3.5 to 4.5. Sphagnum is sterile and light-weight, with a high water-holding capacity, 10 to 20 times its own weight. This material is shredded or ground prior to its use. Sphagnum moss is often used as a germination medium to prevent "damping off" of seedlings. Sphagnum moss by its very nature has some fungistatic properties.

Another material which is often sold under the term peat is better known as Hypnum or Hypnum peat and is composed of decomposed plants from the genus Hypnum and may often include a few mosses and sedges. The pH of hypnum peats is neutral to slightly alkaline and light-brown to greenish-brown in color. They tend to decompose readily and this is not considered desirable for most propagation uses.

The third type of peat is reed-sedge peat and is the decomposition product of sedge, reeds, rushes, cattails and various grasses. Reed-sedge peats decompose rapidly and as a result are seldom used in the nursery industry. A fourth type of peat is known as shrub-tree peat. It is a heterogenous mixture usually composed of the remains of a number of ericaceous plants but may include various willows and alders. It is not a uniform product and as a result is seldom used in the preparation of propagation media.

The last material which is often sold as peat is usually termed muck. Commercial muck peats are generally the advanced stages of decomposed reed-sedge peats with an extremely black color. These are often sold under the term "Michigan Peat". One can easily determine if a material is in fact peat or muck by simply rubbing a small amount of the material between the fingers. If the material smears and leaves a black stain it is muck and not peat. The mucks are generally sold in bags or bales containing 30 to 70% moisture by weight with a nitrogen content ranging from 1 to 3.5%.

The uses of peat are numerous and generally fall into four categories. Initially peats are used as soil conditioners in order to increase or regulate the organic content of soil. They are also used as mulches from 0.6 to 5 cm (0.25 to 2 in) in depth. Sphagnum peat is also used where one desires to grow acid-loving plants including Azaleas, Rhododendrons, Pieris, Heath, Heather, Enkianthus, etc. In addition, peats are commonly used in propagation media.

Another material commonly found in propagation and growing media is vermiculite, a form of expanded mica. Vermiculite is made by heating mica to 1100°C (2000°F) so the alumna-silica plates expand, resulting in a light, fluffy, sterile product with little nutrient value and a pH near neutral. While vermiculite comes in a number of grades, the number 2 grade with the size of a 2 to 3 mm in diameter is usually considered the horticultural grade and is used widely in propagation. Vermiculite has one disadvantage in that it has a tendency with time to lose its structure and when used in potting mixtures has a tendency to eventually compress. Vermiculite generally weighs 96 to 160 kg/cu m (6 to 10 lbs/cu ft), has available K, Mg, and micronutrients, and has a very high exchange capacity.

Another material commonly found in both propagation media and growing media is perlite, a white-gray material of volcanic origin mined from lava flows. Upon heating to 1000°C (1800°F), the lava particles expand yielding a sterile material with a pH near 7.0. Unlike vermiculite, perlite has no cation exchange capacity or nutrient value, and does not have a tendency to break down or compress with prolonged use.

Other materials which can be used as soil amendments include leaf mold or composted leaves. However, this type of material may contain nematodes, various insects, disease organisms, and weeds so it must be sterilized before use. In addition, calcined clay or turface is a montmorillite clay baked at an extremely high temperature and it can be used as an addition to growing or propagating media.

One of the more common materials being used to a greater extent today in propagation or growing media are the various types of bark. These barks can either be pine, fir, redwood, or hardwood mixtures. The barks are used in soil mixes much like peat, but exhibit a much slower rate of decay. When using hardwood bark, it is generally composted prior to use while fir, pine and redwood bark are not commonly composted prior to usage.

MEDIA FOR CONTAINER GROWING

Sometimes following propagation, rooted cuttings or young seedlings are directly planted in the field, but more frequently they are placed in containers for continued growth. For this reason, it is necessary to consider soil and artificial media for growing plant materials.

Field soil, particularly loam and sandy loam, may be included in the soil mixture for container growing but are generally considered unsatisfactory if used unamended. Most soils are too heavy and poorly aerated and may have a rather low moisture holding capacity. In addition, soil becomes sticky after wetting, as well as shrinking upon drying, thus pulling away from the sides of the container and making it difficult to rewet the soil mass. Generally, if soil is used, it is amended with sand and some form of organic matter such as peat, wood shavings, or bark in order to improve its moisture holding capacity.

The more traditional potting mixtures that have been used for the growing of rooted cuttings or seedlings are:

General Potting Mixture A
1 or 2 parts coarse sand
1 part loam or sandy loam soil
1 part sphagnum peat

General Potting Mixture B
1 part coarse sand
2 parts loam or sandy loam soil
1 part sphagnum peat

The physical and chemical properties of mixes such as these vary from batch to batch and cultural problems may arise. In addition, it is necessary that these soil mixtures be steam sterilized prior to the potting operation.

More commonly used with the floricultural crops and for seed germination are the Cornell Peat-Lite mixes. These soilless mixtures are excellent for seed germination and for the production of spring bedding plants. Their greatest assets are that the component parts of the Cornell Peat-Lite mixes are readily available, light-weight, uniform, and have the necessary chemical and physical properties for proper plant growth. Excellent results are obtained with these soilless mixtures which can be prepared from locally available materials or purchased as ready-mixed preparations. In addition, a great advantage to the Cornell Peat-Lite mixes is that the ingredients are sterile so no sterilization is required prior to planting.

Cornell Peat-Lite Mixture A
[To make 0.76 cu m (1 cu yd)]
Shredded Sphagnum Peat - 0.39 cu m (11 Bu)
Horticultural Grade Vermiculite - 0.39 cu m (11 Bu)
Limestone (Dolomitic Lime) - 2.27 kg (5 lb)
Superphosphate - 0.45 kg (1 lb)
5-10-5 fertilizer - 0.91-5.44 kg (2-12 lb)
Fritted trace elements - 57-85 g (2-3 oz)

Cornell Peat-Lite Mixture B
Shredded Sphagnum Peat – 0.39 cu m (11 Bu)
Horticultural Grade Perlite - 0.39 cu m (11 Bu)
Limestone (Dolomitic Lime) - 2.27 kg (5 lb)
Superphosphate - 0.45 kg (1 lb)
5-10-5 fertilizer - 0.91-5.44 kg (2-12 lb)
Fritted trace elements - 57-85 g (2-3 oz)

These Cornell Peat-Lite mixes should be mixed thoroughly prior to usage, and particular attention should be given to wetting the peat in the mix. The use of a non-ionic wetting agent such as Aqua-Gro at 28 g per 22.7 l (1 oz per 6 gal) of water is usually sufficient to initially wet the peat.

For potting young rooted cuttings or seedlings, a mixture of 1 or 2 parts sand, 1 part loam soil and 1 part peat is satisfactory. In addition, one should be familiar with the U-C soil mixes used extensively in California. These mixes, as such, are not used to any great extent in the eastern United States because of the lack of fine sand. The U-C soil mixes are generally based on the availability of very uniform and readily available materials so that the mixture can be easily duplicated. The major component includes fine sand ranging in size from 0.5 to 0.05 mm in diameter, finely ground peat or redwood bark and fertilizer. The basic U-C soil mix is a 50/50 mixture of peat and fine sand.

In conclusion, one could make the following suggestions:
1) Numerous types of media can be effectively used for rooting cuttings.
2) Aeration and drainage are two of the most critical properties of any medium.
3) The success or failure of a medium is dependent upon both its physical and chemical properties and the management program.
4) There is no mystical significance associated with a given medium for a specific plant.

SELECTED REFERENCE MATERIALS

Baker, K. F. (editor). 1957. The U.C. system for producing healthy container-grown plants. Calif. Agri. Expt. Sta. Manual 23.
Boodley, J. W. and R. Sheldrake, Jr. 1964. Cornell "Peat-Lite" mixes for container growing. Cornell University Mimeo Rept.

Chadwick, L. C. 1949. The effect of certain mediums and watering methods on the rooting of cuttings of some deciduous and evergreen plants. Proc. Amer. Soc. Hort. Sci. 53:555-556.

Gray, H. 1967. Exploring rooting media. Proc. Inter. Plant Prop. Soc. 17: 365-366.

Hitchcock, A. E. 1928. Effect of peat moss and sand on rooting response of cuttings. Bot. Gaz. 86:121-148.

Houston, R. and L. C. Chadwick. 1947. Some results of the effects of controlled humidity, mediums and watering methods on the rooting of cuttings of some deciduous and evergreen plants. Proc. Amer. Soc. Hort. Sci. 49: 410-416.

Long, J. C. 1932. The influence of rooting media on the character of roots produced by cuttings. Proc. Amer. Soc. Hort. Sci. 29:352-355.

Matkin, O. A. 1966. Soil mixes. Proc. Inter. Plant Prop. Soc. 15:65-70.

Murphy, J. D., J. B. Gartner and M. M. Meyer. 1969. Comparisons of various individual media for direct rooting of cuttings. Proc. Inter. Plant Prop. Soc. 19:279-283.

Olsen, C. M. 1964. Aerated steam treatment of soil - its principles and application. Proc. Inter. Plant Prop. Soc. 14:305-308.

O'Rourke, F. L. S. and R. R. Dedolph. 1965. Comparative efficacy of two rooting compounds and different media for root induction with greenwood cuttings of seven species. Proc. Amer. Soc. Hort. Sci. 86:815-817.

O'Rourke, F. L. S. and M. A. Maxon. 1948. Effect of particle size of vermiculite media on the rooting of cuttings. Proc. Amer. Soc. Hort. Sci. 51: 654-655.

Osborne, W. W. 1961. Soil sterilization and fumigation. Proc. Inter. Plant Prop. Soc. 11:57-67.

Peterson, F. H. 1966. Commercial application of aerated steam. Proc. Inter. Plant Prop. Soc. 16:70-75.

Pridham, A. M. S. 1948. Comparison of quartz sand, cinders and vermiculite in rooting of evergreen cuttings. Proc. Amer. Soc. Hort. Sci. 51:657-658.

Read, P. E. and R. Sheldrake, Jr. 1966. Correction of chlorosis in plants grown in Cornell peat-lite mixes. Proc. Amer. Soc. Hort. Sci. 88:576-581.

Reisch, K. W. 1967. Rooting media. Proc. Inter. Plant Prop. Soc. 17:356-363.

Robinson, E. H. 1967. Peat-perlite as a rooting media. Proc. Inter. Plant Prop. Soc. 17:363-364.

Vermeulen, J. P. 1965. Rooting - growing media. Proc. Inter. Plant Prop. Soc. 15:97-104.

LABORATORY PROJECT II. PHYSICAL PROPERTIES OF SOME MEDIA.

The physical properties of a propagating medium, besides providing physical support for the cutting or seedling, must also have sufficient properly sized pore spaces to enable the developing root cells to obtain water and oxygen from the air.

PURPOSE:
To determine the density, total pore space, water held at "field capacity" and air space at "field capacity".

MATERIALS:
Paper cups (7 oz size or larger)
Graduated cylinders
Balance or scale
Fine-mesh screen
Pencil
Containers of: a) Perlite
                   b) Vermiculite
                   c) Sphagnum Peat
                   d) Milled Sphagnum Moss
                   e) Sand
                   f) Cornell Peat-lite Mix A
                   g) Soil-Sand-Peat (1:1:1)

PROCEDURE:
1. Weigh a paper cup and record the weight on the chart following these instructions.
2. Pour 200 ml of water into the cup. (Remember 1 ml of water = 1 g)
3. Mark the water level on the cup and discard the water.
4. Fill the cup to the level marked with a selected medium and firm the medium slightly.
5. Weigh the cup, including medium, and record.
6. Subtract cup weight from weight obtained in step 5 and record the medium weight.
7. Then divide by 200 and record. This equals density (weight/volume).
8. Using a graduated cylinder, carefully pour water over the medium until all the pore spaces are filled. Record volume of water required. This volume equals total pore space of the medium.
9. Carefully invert the paper cup and contents over a screen and let all free water drain off.
10. After thoroughly draining, re-weigh the container and medium.
11. Subtract the medium weight (from step 6) from the weight obtained in step 10 and record. This difference equals water held at "field capacity".
12. Subtract water held at "field capacity" from total pore space. This difference equals air space at "field capacity".

RESULTS:
1. Record data in chart provided.

Medium Tested	Results	Step 1: Weight of paper cup (g)	Step 5: Weight of cup and medium (g)	Step 6: Weight of medium (g)	Step 7: Medium weight ÷ 200 = Density	Step 8: Water volume required = Total Pore Space (ml)	Step 10: Drained weight (g)	Step 11: Drained weight minus medium weight (from 6) = water held at "field capacity"	Step 12: Total pore space (from 8) minus water held at "field capacity" (from 11) = air space at "field capacity"

31

THOUGHT PROVOKERS

1. Compare the data for the several media. Can you suggest how these data may influence rooting of cuttings or root development of seedlings?

2. Based on data from this project, discuss the relative merits of the various media and suggest reasons for the use of a specific medium.

LABORATORY PROJECT III.   EVALUATION OF TYPES OF ROOTING MEDIA.

Before becoming either a proficient or skilled propagator, you must determine under grower conditions the best possible medium to use for the rooting process. This medium, as has been discussed, must provide support for the cuttings, and be sufficiently aerated and well-drained, yet retain adequate moisture for rooting to occur. In addition, once you are managing a propagation facility, such considerations as cost, availability, reproducibility, ease of management, freedom from insect, disease and toxic substances, and the ability to be sterilized prior to repeated use must be evaluated prior to selection of the propagation media.

PURPOSE:

To illustrate the functions of a propagation medium, identify the more common types of ingredients, and evaluate the rooting response of cuttings to different media maintained under the same propagation conditions.

MATERIALS:

Chrysanthemum (Chrysanthemum morifolium) cuttings or similar easy to
   root materials
Flats of: a) Vermiculite (or Perlite)
            b) Sand
            c) Sphagnum Peat
            d) Sphagnum Peat-Vermiculite (1:1 by volume)
            e) Sphagnum Peat-Vermiculite-Sand (1:1:1 by volume)
Labels
Propagation Knife
Pencil

PROCEDURE:

1. Prepare a label for each treatment, making sure you include your last name, date, and treatment. Use Pencil only.
2. Select 25 uniform cuttings and divide them into 5 equal groups.
3. Recut the base of each cutting.
4. Stick the cuttings (2-3 cm depth) into each of the 5 rooting media with the appropriate label placed in front.
5. Firm the medium around the base of the cuttings.
6. Place each flat on the bench under mist.

RESULTS:

1. After 2 weeks carefully remove each group of rooted cuttings from the flats and wash the roots with water. Use your labels to keep them in groups.
2. Evaluate the cuttings on a 1-5 visual rating scale. Record the results on the data summary sheet and complete the bar graph.
3. Evaluate the cuttings by counting the number of roots initiated on each and record your results on the data summary sheet.

DATA SUMMARY

	CUTTING NUMBER	VISUAL RATING	NUMBER ROOTS		CUTTING NUMBER	VISUAL RATING	NUMBER ROOTS
VERMICULITE				**SAND**			
	1				1		
	2				2		
	3				3		
	4				4		
	5				5		
	TOTAL				TOTAL		
	MEAN				MEAN		

	CUTTING NUMBER	VISUAL RATING	NUMBER ROOTS		CUTTING NUMBER	VISUAL RATING	NUMBER ROOTS
SPHAGNUM MOSS				**SPHAGNUM MOSS-VERMICULITE (1:1)**			
	1				1		
	2				2		
	3				3		
	4				4		
	5				5		
	TOTAL				TOTAL		
	MEAN				MEAN		

SPHAGNUM MOSS-VERMICULITE-SAND (1:1:1)

	CUTTING NUMBER	VISUAL RATING	NUMBER ROOTS
	1		
	2		
	3		
	4		
	5		
	TOTAL		
	MEAN		

DATA EVALUATION

Prepare bar graphs of your results from the experiment and answer the Thought Provokers.

A) Effect of various propagation media on the mean visual evaluation of rooting.

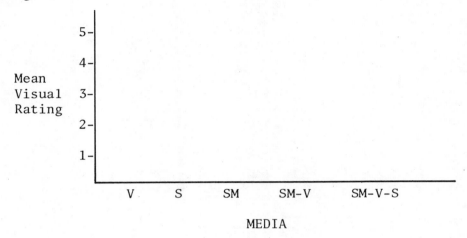

B) Effect of various propagation media on the number of roots produced.

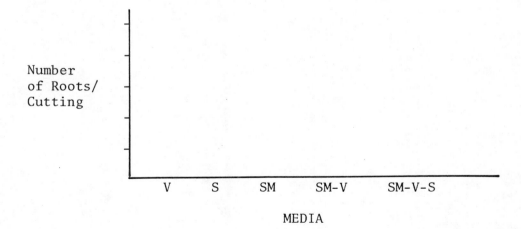

THOUGHT PROVOKERS

1. Fill in the table on the following page for background information before answering the following questions.

2. What are the physical and chemical characteristics of the treatment (medium) that exhibited the best rooting response? The poorest rooting response? Why do you expect that this medium gave the best results?

3. The frequency and duration of the mist system is set for rooting cuttings in a sand medium. In the following production cycle a sphagnum vermiculite medium (1:1) is used instead of sand. With all other factors remaining the same, how will the rooting response be altered? (Assume the media were properly prepared for use.) How would you correct any problem that exists?

4. List 3 characteristics of soil that would limit its use as a suitable rooting medium.

5. If you were to root cuttings in a flat and overwinter these cuttings in this same flat what medium would you use and why?

TABLE 3. PHYSICAL CHARACTERISTICS OF ROOTING MEDIUM INGREDIENTS.

Character-istics Medium	Weight (dry)		Water Holding Capacity		pH			Drainage		Other (At least 3 characteristics)	Origin
	Light	Heavy	Low	High	Low	Neutral	High	Good	Poor		
Perlite											
Sand											
Sphagnum Peat											
Vermiculite											

LABORATORY PROJECT IV. A DEMONSTRATION OF THE PRINCIPLE OF AERATION ON ROOT PRODUCTION.

The rooting medium has a number of important functions, of which the allowance of air to penetrate to the base of the cutting is one of the most important. For a rooting medium to be considered "ideal" it must provide sufficient porosity to allow good aeration.

Numerous researchers have noted that cuttings of several species of woody plants respond quite differently when the oxygen available in the rooting medium is varied.

PURPOSE:

To explain (or illustrate) the role and need for oxygen in the rooting process.

MATERIALS:

15 cm (6 in) long mung bean (Phaseolus aureus) or willow (Salix sp.) cuttings
25 cm (10 in) test tubes
Aquarium pump, valve, tygon tubing and air stones
Grease pencil
Ruler - metric
Propagation knife

PROCEDURE:

1. Prepare 2 sets of test tubes and fill with distilled water to a depth of 5, 10 and 20 cm (2, 4 and 8 in).
2. Place air stones in one set of the test tubes.
3. Insert 5 cuttings of either mung bean or willow into each test tube.
4. Mark the water depth with a grease pencil.
5. Using the pump and air stones, aerate one set of the test tubes with cuttings and let the other set act as the control group.
6. Observe the cuttings frequently and keep the water in the test tubes at the proper predetermined levels.

RESULTS:

1. After 1-2 weeks observe the rooting which has occurred in the aerated and non-aerated tubes at the various water depths.
2. Evaluate the cuttings by counting the number of roots per cutting and obtaining their length in centimeters. Record your results in the data summary table.

DATA SUMMARY

AERATED			NON-AERATED		
TREATMENT	NUMBER ROOTS	LENGTH ROOTS (CM)	TREATMENT	NUMBER ROOTS	LENGTH ROOTS (CM)

5 CM (2 IN) WATER

AERATED			NON-AERATED		
1			1		
2			2		
3			3		
4			4		
5			5		
TOTAL			TOTAL		
MEAN			MEAN		

10 CM (4 IN) WATER

AERATED			NON-AERATED		
1			1		
2			2		
3			3		
4			4		
5			5		
TOTAL			TOTAL		
MEAN			MEAN		

20 CM (8 IN) WATER

AERATED			NON-AERATED		
1			1		
2			2		
3			3		
4			4		
5			5		
TOTAL			TOTAL		
MEAN			MEAN		

44

DATA EVALUATION

1. Prepare bar graphs based on an evaluation of your results. Plot the treatment means on your graphs.

A) Effect of aeration on the mean number of roots per cutting.

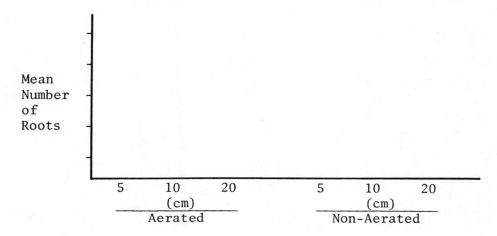

B) Effect of aeration and on the mean root length in cm.

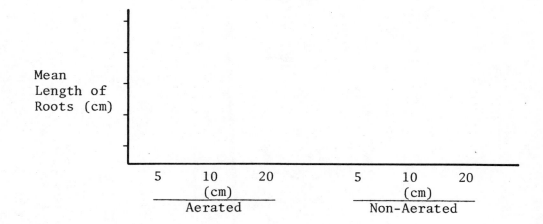

THOUGHT PROVOKERS

1. What differences in root development did you observe as a result of
    aeration of the rooting medium and why?

2. How might you relate your results in this experiment to the results you
    obtained earlier in the Experiment entitled "Evaluation of the Types of
    Rooting Media"?

Asexual Propagation of Cuttings

Asexual or vegetative propagation of plants by cuttings is a very important part of horticultural science. Asexual techniques allow the increase of plants so that all propagules are genetically identical to the parents. This differs greatly from sexual propagation where there remains the potential for diverse genetic variation. Seedling populations from a great many horticultural crops are so variable, that asexual propagation affords the only way to practically maintain these individuals in order to retain their uniformity.

The basic task in horticultural propagation is to renew and regenerate plants by using a piece of tissue so that the final product will result in a new self-supporting individual. Obviously, the difficulty in this task involves the proper selection of tissues and the techniques themselves.

Cuttings can be made from stem, leaf and root tissues. In the rooting of stem cuttings one is involved in obtaining a detached plant part and placing it under conditions conducive to the regeneration of its missing parts, i.e., roots, to form a new, self-sustaining individual. In this case the cutting has been removed from a functioning root system and as a result the major life-support problem for this cutting becomes one of water relations. As a result of the loss of its connection to a viable root system, there is little or no water uptake by the cutting although transpiration or the loss of water to the surrounding atmosphere by the vegetative portion of the cutting will continue.

Cuttings are quite diverse in their form, and can be obtained from all vegetative portions of the plant, including roots, stems, modified stems such as bulbs, tubers or corms, and leaves.

STEM CUTTINGS

Stem cuttings are the most important and greatest used type of cutting. In general, they can be divided into 4 groups, the hardwood, semi-hardwood, softwood or herbaceous and the cane cutting. When preparing a stem cutting a section of stem tissue with lateral or terminal buds is obtained. Typically, stem cuttings are made from the terminal ends of shoots, generally 8-13 cm (3-5 in) long and are removed from the parent plant at a point just below a healthy leaf. As a general rule, the stem cutting (except hardwood and cane types) should have 3 to 4 leaves for quickest rooting. The leaves from the basal 1/3 of the stem cutting should be removed.

DECIDUOUS HARDWOOD CUTTINGS

Hardwood cuttings are prepared from the mature stems of various trees and shrubs and provide one of the easiest and least expensive means of propagation (Figure 12 A-G). These cuttings are prepared during the dormant season using wood from the previous season's growth, although in a few cases, older wood can be used. The length of hardwood cuttings vary from 10-30 cm (4-12 in), but cuttings of plants such as willow and some fruit stock can be as long as 0.6-0.9 m (2-3 ft). In most cases, cuttings of pencil thickness, i.e., 0.6-1.2 cm (1/4-1/2 in) in diameter with at least 2 nodes are selected depending upon the species.

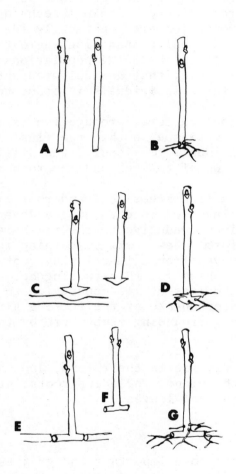

FIGURE 12. DECIDUOUS HARDWOOD CUTTINGS. A & B - THE STRAIGHT HARDWOOD; C & D - THE HEEL HARDWOOD; AND E, F & G - THE MALLET HARDWOOD CUTTING.

Three types of hardwood cuttings can be prepared, the straight (Figure 12 A & B), the heel (Figure 12 C & D), and the mallet (Figure 12 E, F & G) cutting. The heel hardwood cutting has attached at its base a small portion of older wood, while the mallet hardwood cutting includes a short section of older stem wood. The straight hardwood cutting is entirely composed of 1 year wood.

Hardwood cuttings are often used to propagate deciduous shrubs such as forsythia, weigela, privet, dogwood, spirea, and honeysuckle. In addition, fruit species such as quince, grape, gooseberry, currant and plum are also propagated commercially using the hardwood cutting.

NARROWLEAF EVERGREEN HARDWOOD CUTTINGS

Narrowleaf evergreen hardwood cuttings are usually 10-20 cm (4-8 in) long with the foliage removed from the basal 1/3 to 1/2 of the cutting. In general, this type cutting is gathered in the late fall or early winter from mature terminal shoots of the previous season's growth. Plants which are propagated in this manner include false cypress, yew, arborvitae, spruce, hemlock, fir, pine and juniper.

SEMI-HARDWOOD CUTTINGS

Woody, broadleaf evergreens propagated in mid-summer from partially matured wood and leafy summer cuttings from mature tissue are often termed semi-hardwood cuttings. Ornamentals propagated in this manner include the deciduous and evergreen azaleas, euonymus, camellia and holly (Figure 13).

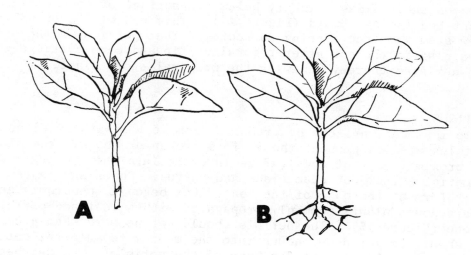

FIGURE 13.   SEMI-HARDWOOD CUTTING OF RHODODENDRON.

Semi-hardwood cuttings are prepared from terminal or lateral branches 8-15 cm (3-6 in) long. The leaves are removed from the basal 1/3 to 1/2 of the cuttings. With plants that have large leaves, the leaves can be cut in half thereby reducing transpirational losses and allowing closer spacing in the propagation bed.

SOFTWOOD OR HERBACEOUS CUTTINGS

When cuttings are prepared from the soft, succulent, herbaceous growth they are termed softwood, herbaceous or greenwood cuttings. An extremely wide range of horticultural plants are propagated in this manner including chrysanthemums, hydrangea, fuschia, and geraniums among the greenhouse crops and forsythia, privet, pyracantha, lilac, magnolia, weigela, spirea, cotoneaster, and dogwood to name a few among the ornamental landscape plants.

These cuttings are prepared much the same as semi-hardwood cuttings described above. They are generally 8-13 cm (3-5 in) in length with the leaves retained on the upper 2/3 to 1/2 of the cutting. The herbaceous or softwood cutting should have 2 or more nodes and like the semi-hardwood cutting, if the leaves are large, they may be cut in half in order to reduce water loss through transpiration and save space.

CANE CUTTINGS

Cane cuttings are a form of stem cutting used to propagate dumbcane, Chinese evergreen, dracaena, and similar plants which produce long cane-like stems. The cane which remains after a tip or stem cutting is removed from the parent plant can be cut off about 8 cm (3 in) above the soil line. This portion of stem or cane is then cut into small sections 5-8 cm (2-3 in) long so that each piece has at least two leaf scars and a dormant bud. The stem sections are placed on their sides slightly below the surface of the rooting medium with the dormant bud facing upward (Figure 14). This bud will eventually sprout and form a new stem when the cutting is rooted. That portion of the original stock plant remaining in the pot after removal of tip and cane cuttings will sprout to form a new stem thereby renewing the original stock plant.

LEAF CUTTINGS

Whole leaf cuttings can be prepared from leaves with or without petioles. When petioles are not present the leaf is broken or cut off the plant and the basal or proximal edge of the leaf is inserted into the rooting medium. Plants without petioles include sedum, jade and cactus. Roots and leaves will eventually form at the base of the leaf. Rex begonia, peperomia and African violets are house plants commonly propagated with a leaf and petiole or leaf blade alone (Figure 15). The petiole should not be more than 4 cm (1.5 in) long and should be set deep enough into the medium to keep the cutting erect. Roots and leaves will form at the base of the petiole. The Rex begonia may also be propagated by laying the whole leaf on the rooting medium and severing the major veins with a knife. At each place where the cut vein touches the medium a new plant will be produced (Figure 16).

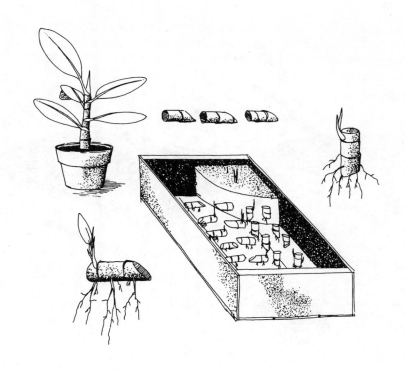

FIGURE 14.   PREPARATION OF CANE CUTTINGS

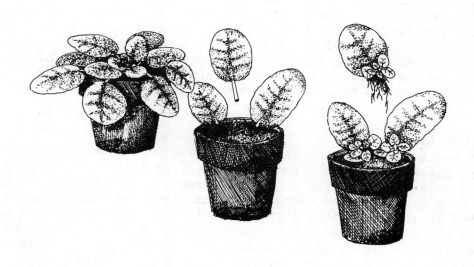

FIGURE 15.   LEAF CUTTING OF AFRICAN VIOLET
WITH THE PETIOLE ATTACHED.

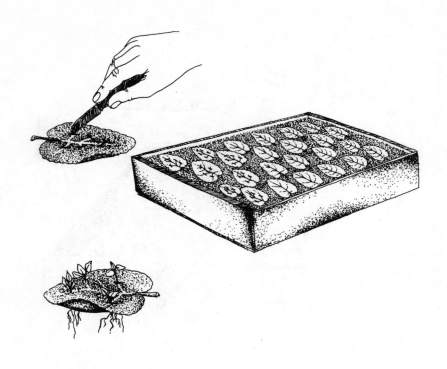

FIGURE 16.   LEAF CUTTING OF REX BEGONIA.

     In addition, leaf cuttings can be prepared by taking leaf sections when propagating plants like Rex begonia and snake plant (Sansevieria sp.). The leaves of a snake plant, for example, are cut into pieces 5-8 cm (2-3 in) long making certain that the proximal edge is inserted into the rooting medium (Figure 17). Leaves of the Rex begonia are cut into wedge shaped pieces with each piece containing a main vein. Once again the edge of the cutting closest to the parent plant is inserted into the rooting medium. Roots and new leaves form at the base of these cuttings (Figure 18).

LEAF-BUD CUTTINGS

     Leaf-bud cuttings can be used to increase such plants as English ivy, grape ivy, geranium, philodendron, peperomia, rhododendron, hydrangea, and others. The leaf bud cutting as the name implies consists of a single leaf attached to a piece of stem tissue 2.5-4 cm (1-1.5 in) long (Figure 19). A dormant bud is located in the axil of the leaf and will give rise to the new shoot. In the case of plants with opposite leaves, the stem can be cut down the middle thus resulting in two leaf-bud cuttings. If both leaves are left on the cutting it is sometimes referred to as a stub cutting.

FIGURE 17.   LEAF CUTTING OF SNAKE PLANT (SANSEVIERIA SP.).

FIGURE 18.   LEAF SECTION CUTTINGS OF REX BEGONIA.

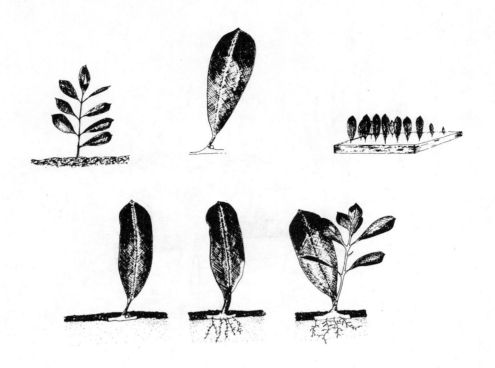

FIGURE 19. LEAF BUD CUTTINGS OF RHODODENDRON.

ROOT CUTTINGS

Root cuttings are applicable for the propagation of more woody plants than is commonly realized. They are also beneficial as a means of propagating fruit rootstocks. In addition, they play a particularly important role in the propagation of herbaceous perennials.

Root cuttings are usually obtained during the dormant season from young stock plants when the roots are well supplied with carbohydrates. Once the soil is removed from the root system by shaking or washing, the cuttings are then prepared by cutting to a length of about 10 cm (4 in), although cuttings from plants such as phlox, anemones, and gaillardias may be smaller. The stock plants are commonly reset into the beds after the excess roots have been removed.

Root cuttings may be thickly planted in rows in cold frames, placing the cuttings in a vertical position with the proximal end of the cutting just below the medium surface (Figure 20). Other techniques involve spreading the root cuttings horizontally on the medium surface, and when using this technique, orientation of the cuttings need not be considered.

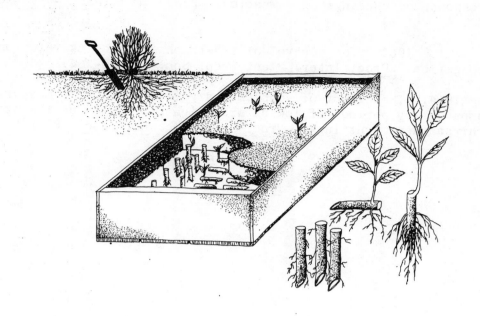

FIGURE 20.   PREPARATION OF ROOT CUTTINGS.

SELECTED REFERENCE MATERIALS

Briggs, B. A. 1966. An experiment in air-rooting. Proc. Inter. Plant Prop. Soc. 16:139-141.

Chadwick. L. C. 1953. The fundamentals of propagating deciduous shrubs by hardwood cuttings. Proc. Inter. Plant Prop. Soc. 3:120-133.

Fillmore, R. H. 1965. Position in cutting selection. Proc. Inter. Plant Prop. Soc. 15:232-233.

Hess, C. E. 1963. Why certain plants are hard to root. Proc. Inter. Plant Prop. Soc. 13:63-71.

O'Rourke, F. L. S. 1940. The influence of blossom buds on rooting of hardwood cuttings of blueberry. Proc. Amer. Soc. Hort. Sci. 40:332-335.

O'Rourke, F. L. S. 1944. Wood type and original position on shoot with reference to rooting in hardwood cuttings of blueberry. Proc. Amer. Soc. Hort. Sci. 45:195-197.

Pokorny, F. A. and J. R. Kamp. 1965. Influence of photoperiod on the rooting response of cuttings of carnation. <u>Proc</u>. <u>Amer</u>. <u>Soc</u>. <u>Hort</u>. <u>Sci</u>. 86:626-630.

Stoutemeyer, V. T. 1962. The control of growth phases and its relation to plant propagation. <u>Proc</u>. <u>Inter</u>. <u>Plant</u> <u>Prop</u>. <u>Soc</u>. 12:260-264.

Swain, G. S. 1964. The effect of supplementary illumination by mercury vapour lamps during periods of low natural light intensity on the production of chrysanthemum cuttings. <u>Proc</u>. <u>Amer</u>. <u>Soc</u>. <u>Hort</u>. <u>Sci</u>. 85:568-573.

<u>NOTES</u>

LABORATORY PROJECT V. TYPE OF CUTTINGS.

PURPOSE:
    To demonstrate the different types of cuttings which can be prepared
from various types of plant materials and the methods of preparing the various
types of cuttings.

MATERIALS:
    Plant material (See Appendix II and III)
    Propagation knife
    Labels
    Pencil
    Rooting hormone
    Propagation medium in flats

PROCEDURE:
    1. Prepare examples of each of the following types of cuttings.
            Leaf-bud cuttings
            Leaf cuttings
            Leaf section cuttings (leaf piece)
            Cane cuttings
            Herbaceous or softwood stem cuttings
    2. Prepare the following types of cuttings
            Deciduous hardwood stem cuttings
            Semi-hardwood stem cuttings
            Leaf bud cuttings
            Narrowleaf evergreen stem cuttings
            Root cuttings

THOUGHT PROVOKERS

1. Horticulturally, what can be done to "harden-off" herbaceous or softwood cuttings prior to planting them outdoors?

2. With the leaf piece or leaf section cutting, where does the new adventitious shoot system arise?

3. When propagating the variegated Sansevieria from leaf cuttings typically non-variegated plants develop. Explain how and why this occurs. How is the variegated form of Sansevieria propagated?

4. Explain <u>why</u> and <u>when</u> you would recommend each of the following types of cuttings:

Leaf-bud cutting

Leaf section cutting

Cane cutting

Deciduous hardwood stem cutting

5. Coleus and several other plants do not form an adventitious bud from the petiole attached to a leaf cutting. Because of this fact, how would you propagate these plants?

6. Which of the cuttings that you prepared in this laboratory exercise takes the longest to produce a saleable plant? Why?

LABORATORY PROJECT VI.   INFLUENCE OF LEAF AREA ON ROOT DEVELOPMENT.

It has long been known that the presence of leaves on cuttings has a highly promotive effect on root initiation and development. Carbohydrates produced via photosynthesis are translocated from the leaf tissue and certainly contribute to root development. However, the effects of leaves on root-promoting effects are probably due to other, more direct, factors. Leaves and buds are known to produce large quantities of auxins which are translocated basipetally so that the effects of the auxins are observed directly below the leaves, i.e., in the areas where root initiation occurs.

PURPOSE:
To compare the effects of leaves on the rooting responses of cuttings.

MATERIALS:
Chrysanthemum (C. morifolium) cuttings
Propagation knife
Labels
Pencil
Propagation medium in flats

PROCEDURE:
1. Print a label for each treatment.
    Treatments
    4 leaves
    3 leaves
    2 leaves
    1 leaf
    0 leaves
2. Select 25 uniform cuttings.
3. Remove leaves to get the desired number for each treatment.
4. Recut the base of each cutting.
5. Stick the cuttings into the propagation flat with the appropriate label.
6. Firm the medium around the base of the cuttings.
7. Place the propagation flat on the bench under mist.
8. Inspect your cuttings regularly.

RESULTS:
1. After 2 weeks carefully remove the rooted cuttings from the flat and wash the roots with water.
2. Evaluate the cuttings on a 1-5 visual rating scale and record your results on the data summary sheet.
3. Evaluate the cuttings by counting the number of roots per cutting and record the results on the data summary sheet.

DATA SUMMARY

	CUTTING NUMBER	VISUAL RATING	NUMBER ROOTS		CUTTING NUMBER	VISUAL RATING	NUMBER ROOTS
4 LEAVES				**1 LEAF**			
	1				1		
	2				2		
	3				3		
	4				4		
	5				5		
	TOTAL				TOTAL		
	MEAN				MEAN		
3 LEAVES				**0 LEAVES**			
	1				1		
	2				2		
	3				3		
	4				4		
	5				5		
	TOTAL				TOTAL		
	MEAN				MEAN		
2 LEAVES							
	1						
	2						
	3						
	4						
	5						
	TOTAL						
	MEAN						

64

DATA EVALUATION

1. Prepare bar graphs based on an evaluation of your results from this experiment. Plot in this graph the mean values for the various treatments.

   A) Effect of leaf area on the mean visual rating of the rooting response of cuttings.

   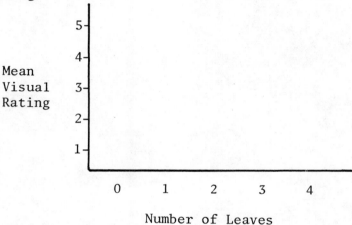

   B) Effect of leaf area on the mean number of roots initiated.

   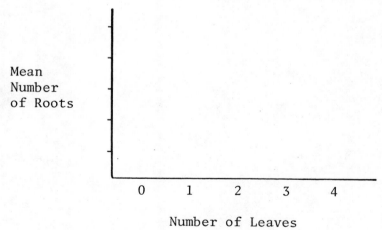

THOUGHT PROVOKERS

1. What effect did the number of leaves have on rooting? Your answer should be in detail and state the reasons for these results.

2. How would the addition of a growth regulator such as IBA to the base of the cuttings have influenced the results on cuttings with 0, 2 and 4 leaves?

3. Leaf area is known to influence several factors which are important in rooting. What are they and how do they affect rooting?

LABORATORY PROJECT VII.   EVALUATION OF METHODS FOR THE REDUCTION OF WATER LOSS
                           FROM LEAFY CUTTINGS.

Water loss from cuttings is a serious problem, and is commonly overcome by the use of a properly regulated mist system. However, one should realize that there may be alternatives to the fully automated intermittent mist system.

When cuttings are removed from the parent plant, they continue to transpire. Without a root system, cuttings are poorly equipped to obtain water. Prior to the advent of intermittent mist systems, water loss was reduced by frequent wetting of the leaves, reducing the foliage (leaf area) of the cuttings, shading and syringing to maintain a high humidity.

PURPOSE:
     To demonstrate the effect of various methods of reducing or preventing water loss from leafy cuttings.

MATERIALS:
     Chrysanthemum (C. morifolium) or other suitable herbaceous plant material
     Propagation knife
     Wilf-Pruf (1:4 solution)
     Labels
     Propagation medium in flats
     Pencil

PROCEDURE:
     1. Print a label for each of the following treatments.
             Treatments
             A. Anti-transpirant dip
             B. High humidity frame
             C. Intermittent mist
             D. Control
     2. Prepare 40 herbaceous cuttings approximately 10 cm (4 in) in length
        to be treated as follows:
             A. Dip 10 cuttings (completely immerse the cuttings) into a 1:4
                solution of Wilt-Pruf and allow to dry. Stick the cuttings
                into the propagation flat to be placed in the greenhouse.
             B. Stick 10 cuttings in a polyethylene-covered propagation flat.
             C. Stick 10 cuttings in the propagation flat to be placed in the
                intermittent mist bed.
             D. Stick 10 cuttings in a control propagation flat to be placed
                in the greenhouse.
     3. Be sure to firm the medium around the base of the cuttings.
     4. Place the propagation flats in the greenhouse in the proper locations.

RESULTS:
1. After 2 weeks carefully remove the cuttings from the flats and remove any medium adhering to the roots by washing with water.
2. Evaluate the cuttings on a 1-5 visual rating scale and record your results on the data summary sheet.
3. Evaluate the cuttings by counting the number of roots per cutting and record your results on the data summary sheet.

NOTES

DATA SUMMARY

CUTTING NUMBER	VISUAL RATING	NUMBER ROOTS	CUTTING NUMBER	VISUAL RATING	NUMBER ROOTS
ANTI-TRANSPIRANT DIP			**HIGH HUMIDITY FRAME**		
1			1		
2			2		
3			3		
4			4		
5			5		
6			6		
7			7		
8			8		
9			9		
10			10		
TOTAL			TOTAL		
MEAN			MEAN		
INTERMITTENT MIST			**CONTROL**		
1			1		
2			2		
3			3		
4			4		
5			5		
6			6		
7			7		
8			8		
9			9		
10			10		
TOTAL			TOTAL		
MEAN			MEAN		

DATA EVALUATION

1. Prepare the following bar graphs based on the evaluation of your results. Plot on the graphs the mean values you obtained for each treatment.

   A) Effectiveness of various treatments at reducing water loss from cuttings.

   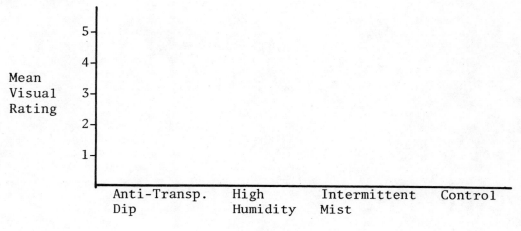

   B. Effectiveness of various treatments on the mean number of roots per cuttings.

   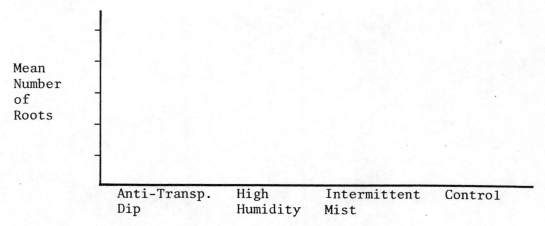

THOUGHT PROVOKERS

1. From the evaluation of your results, which of the treatments employed in this study gave the best results? Why?

2. Do you think that with some modification, the anti-transpirant dip could be substituted for the intermittent mist in the rooting of cuttings?

3. Discuss the way in which anti-transpirants function. How could they adversely affect plant growth over an extended period of time?

4. Distinguish between the terms "reduction of water loss" and "prevention of water loss".

76

LABORATORY PROJECT VIII.   MAINTENANCE OF HEALTHY PLANTING AND ROOTING STOCK
(CULTURE-INDEXING).

During the propagation and production of numerous herbaceous and woody plant materials, it is extremely important to prevent disease infection. To accomplish this, it is imperative that propagators begin with clean stock in the propagation process.

In general, identification of the presence of pathogens can be made in 2 ways. If the pathogen produces a recognizable plant symptom it can be identified initially by visual inspection. (In both cases, the material should be discarded prior to propagation, and efforts should be made to clean up or eliminate the source of the infection.) Secondly, it may be possible where visual symptoms are lacking, to "index" the material in order to ascertain whether or not it is a carrier of a fungal or bacterial disease.

PURPOSE:
To demonstrate a technique for determining the presence of fungal or bacterial organisms on stock plants.

MATERIALS:
Geranium (Pelargonium hortorum) stock plants or other suitable material
Petri dishes
Potato dextrose agar - PDA
0.33% solution sodium hypochlorite (1 part chlorox:16 parts H_2O)
Paper towels
Beakers
Scalpels or razor blades
Alcohol lamp
Forceps
Propagation flats filled with 1:1 Peat-vermiculite

PROCEDURE:
1. From the stock plants available, select and prepare 5 uniform cuttings.
2. For each cutting select a prepared petri dish of PDA and label accordingly.
3. Cut a 2.5 cm (1 in) segment from the base of each cutting and immerse in the 0.33% sodium hypochlorite solution for 3 minutes.
4. Remove the 2.5 cm segments of stem tissue and blot on clean paper towelling.
5. With a flamed scalpel slice 4 - 0.07 cm (1/32 in) pieces from one of the stem segments and transfer them to the assigned petri dish. Repeat this procedure with the other 4 stem segments. Take care to expose the agar to the room environment as briefly as possible. WORK RAPIDLY!
6. Place the cultures in the growth cabinet, at 24-26°C (75-80°F).

7. Label the cuttings and propagate them in flats of peat-vermiculite to be placed under intermittent mist in the greenhouse.
8. Note the condition of the cuttings placed in propagation bench.

RESULTS:
1. After 1 week, make note of any growths on the PDA plates which occurred as a result of infected stem pieces.
2. Record the number and types of growths which occurred.
3. Observe the condition of the rooted cuttings and note if there is any relationship to the cultures on the PDA.

DATA SUMMARY

Culture Number	Number of Colonies	Colony Descriptions
1		
2		
3		
4		
5		

THOUGHT PROVOKERS

1. From your observations, what type of organism(s) do you think are responsible for the growths in the culture?

2. If an infected group of plants was noted among your stock blocks, what course of action would be appropriate?

3. What was the relationship between the rooted cuttings and the cultures observed on the PDA plates?

Juvenility

It has been known by practical plant propagators and horticulurists that cuttings taken from young seedling plants root much more readily than cuttings taken from mature plants of the same species. The term juvenility was first used in 1900 by the German physiologist Goebel, to describe this phenomenon which is associated with the physiological age of a plant rather than its chronological age. In addition, it should be noted that various individual plants progress toward maturity at different rates.

The physiological aspects of juvenility may be associated with outward morphological manifestations such as:
1. Alternate, palmately lobed leaves (juvenile) versus entire, ovate, opposite leaves on mature flowering plants (English ivy).
2. Leaves opposite and entire compared with alternate and toothed leaves on mature plants (Elm).
3. Needle-like leaves instead of scale-like leaves (Junipers).
4. Thinner leaves (many plants).
5. Less pubescence on the leaves (many plants).
6. Greater thorniness (Honeylocust, Black Locust).
7. Tendency for lower branches to root better (many plants).
8. Juvenile bipinnate leaves versus adult expanded petioles called phyllodia (Acacia).

The ability of a plant to produce and maintain two entirely distinct morphological types of foliage in different growth phases (juvenile or mature) has been termed topophysis. In fact these different growth phases can be propagated and perpetuated. Many propagators suggest that the condition of juvenility is responsible for the fact that softwood cuttings taken from young seedlings root more easily than those taken from mature plants of the same species. Listed below are other sources of cuttings which have been found to exhibit juvenile rooting characteristics.
1. Etiolated shoots.
2. Shoots of the current season's growth arising from:
   a. near the base of the plant.
   b. plants that have been cut back severely.
   c. branches from lower portions of a tree.
   d. diseased or injured plants.
   e. adventitious or latent buds.
   f. root pieces.
3. Shoots with sphaeroblasts (wart-like growths containing meristematic and conductive tissue).

Investigations by Stoutmeyer and coworkers have revealed that root cuttings from young honeylocust seedlings sprouted better than those from mature trees although root cuttings taken nearest the crown of mature trees sprouted better than those taken at the distal end of the root system.

It was suggested by Stoutmeyer that the production of such juvenile shoots from root pieces is due possibly to the fact that adventitious buds, from which all root sprouts arise, have no connection with the primary meristematic tissue of the parent plant and therefore possess all of the seedling ontogeny including juvenility. Another assumption is that the juvenile form tends to linger longer in the lower parts of the tree trunk and in the roots.

While cuttings from many plant species, including the apple, are considered to be difficult to root, Stoutmeyer found that those taken from apple sprouts which developed from root pieces rooted readily. In addition, it was also observed that softwood cuttings of honeylocust sprouts grown from root cuttings or from stump sprouts rooted easily while those cuttings taken from the upper portions of trees ordinarily could not be rooted unless from very young seedlings.

Thorniness in seedlings has been reported on citrus and honeylocust seedlings, but at maturity, shoots upward and outward from the trunk gradually lose the thorny condition. O'Rourke cited experiments which indicated that the thorny condition was associated with the juvenile growth phase while the thornless condition denoted the mature phase of growth.

In mid-November, Grace collected branches from the upper and lower one-third portions of an 18 year old Norway Spruce. These were divided into 90 cuttings from each position and placed in a sand medium. Ten weeks later 75% and 43% of the cuttings from the lower and upper positions respectively had rooted. The uprooted cuttings were replaced for another nine weeks. As final values for the experiment, 86% of the cuttings from the lower position and 48% of the cuttings from the upper position had rooted. Wilms and O'Rourke reported that clones of Juniperus and Thuja showing "nodules" on the young stem rooted more readily than cuttings without nodules.

Exact location of juvenility within a plant where the juvenile influence remains longest and exerts its greatest influence appears to be in the basal portion of the trunk extending into the lateral roots. Grace concludes that "it is possible that there are physiological differences in the rooting response of cuttings taken from the upper and lower regions of the spruce, since the upper region bears female flowers, and the lower region male flowers, and the wide spreading lower branches of some varieties have a tendency to layer". These facts suggest that juvenility and the capacity for easy regeneration may be inhibited by biochemical agents which bring about a capacity for reproduction. Since juvenility occurs in both roots and etiolated branch growth, perhaps production of these biochemical agents is lacking under dark conditions.

SELECTED REFERENCE MATERIALS

Grace, M. H. 1939. Vegetative propagation of conifers. I. Rooting of cuttings taken from the upper and the lower regions of a Norway spruce tree. Can. J. Res. 17:178-180.

O'Rourke, F. L. 1952. The effect of juvenility on plant propagation. Nat. Hort. Mag. 31:278-282.

Stoutmeyer, V. T. 1937. Regeneration in various types of apple wood. Iowa Agri. Expt. Sta. Res. Bull. 220.

Stoutmeyer, V. T., F. L. O'Rourke and W. W. Steiner. 1944. Some observations on vegetative propagation of honeylocust. Forestry 42:32-35.

Wilms, G. L. and F. L. O'Rourke. 1960. The effect of nodules on the rooting of cuttings of Juniperus and Thuja. Proc. Inter. Plant Prop. Soc. 10:203-204.

LABORATORY PROJECT IX. INFLUENCE OF TISSUE AGE ON THE ROOTING OF CUTTINGS.

Many plants that are easily propagated are done so with little regard for the age of the stock plant or the age of the tissue. However, in plants that are difficult to propagate the age of the tissue can be an extremely important factor. Quite often stem or root cuttings taken from young seedlings will root more readily than similar material taken from older plants which are in an adult growth phase.

PURPOSE:

To evaluate the rooting response of cuttings taken from plant material of different physiological ages.

MATERIALS:

English ivy (Hedera helix) cuttings from juvenile and mature plants
Propagation medium in flats
Propagation knife
Labels
IBA

PROCEDURE:

1. Prepare a label for each of the following treatments.
    A. Juvenile ivy cuttings
    B. Mature ivy cuttings
2. Select 10 unfiorm cuttings from each group of ivy cuttings.
3. Recut the bases of the cuttings and treat with IBA (Hormodin #2 or equivalent).
4. Stick the cuttings into the propagation flat and firm the medium around the base of the cuttings.
5. Place the propagation flat on the mist bench.

RESULTS:

1. After approximately 4 weeks remove the rooted cuttings from the flat and remove any adhering soil particles by washing with water.
2. Evaluate the cuttings using a 1-5 visual rating scale and record the results on the data summary table.
3. Evaluate the cuttings by counting the number of roots initiated and record the results on the data summary table.

DATA SUMMARY

TREATMENT	CUTTING NUMBER	VISUAL RATING	NUMBER ROOTS
JUVENILE CUTTINGS			
	1		
	2		
	3		
	4		
	5		
	6		
	7		
	8		
	9		
	10		
TOTAL			
MEAN			
MATURE CUTTINGS			
	1		
	2		
	3		
	4		
	5		
	6		
	7		
	8		
	9		
	10		
TOTAL			
MEAN			

DATA EVALUATION

1. Prepare bar graphs based on an evaluation of your results. Plot the mean treatment values in your graphs.

   A) Comparison of juvenile and mature tissue on mean visual evaluation of root production per cutting.

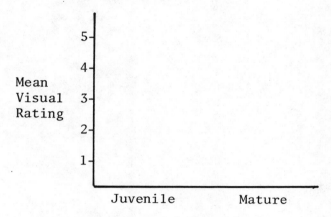

   B) Comparison of juvenile and mature tissue on the mean number of roots produced per cutting.

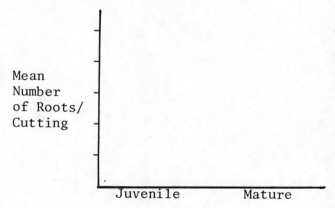

87

THOUGHT PROVOKERS

1. Cite several examples of how juvenility is used to the advantage of the propagator.

2. How can the nurseryman, propagator or researcher hasten this change from the juvenile to adult characteristics?

3. Cite examples of plants which are maintained as juveniles, through continued propagation. Why might this be desirable?

LABORATORY PROJECT X.   EVALUATION OF THE SIZE OF CUTTINGS AND THE TYPE OF
                         WOOD.

PURPOSE:
   To demonstrate the effect that different types of wood and different size
cuttings will have on rooting of cuttings.

MATERIALS:
   Cuttings of Red-Osier Dogwood (Cornus sericea), Forsythia (Forsythia x
      intermedia) or Firethorn (Pyracantha sp.) or similar materials
   Labels
   Pencil
   Propagation knife
   Propagation medium in flats
   Growth regulator or rooting hormone

PROCEDURE:
   1. Prepare a label for each treatment making sure to include your last
      name, date, and treatment. Use PENCIL only.
         Treatments
         A. 15 cm (6 in) cutting
         B. 30 cm (12 in) cutting
         C. 15 cm (6 in) cutting from current season's growth
         D. 15 cm (6 in) cutting from hardened material
   2. Prepare 10 uniform cuttings of each of the above treatments.
   3. Treat each of the cuttings with a rooting growth regulator making sure
      to shake off any excess powder from the base of the cuttings.
   4. Stick the cuttings into the flat of propagation medium.
   5. Firm the medium around the base of the cuttings.
   6. Place in flat on the bench under mist.
   7. Inspect the cuttings regularly to determine when they are ready to
      evaluate.

RESULTS:
   1. After 4-6 weeks carefully remove the cuttings from the propagation
      medium and wash the roots with water.
   2. Evaluate the cuttings with a 1-5 visual rating scale and record your
      results on the data summary sheet.
   3. Evaluate the cuttings by counting the number of roots initiated
      and record your results on the data summary sheet.

DATA SUMMARY

TREATMENT	CUTTING NUMBER	VISUAL RATING	NUMBER ROOTS
A. 15 CM (6 IN) CUTTING	1		
	2		
	3		
	4		
	5		
	6		
	7		
	8		
	9		
	10		
TOTAL			
MEAN			
B. 30 CM (12 IN) CUTTING	1		
	2		
	3		
	4		
	5		
	6		
	7		
	8		
	9		
	10		
TOTAL			
MEAN			
C. 15 CM (6 IN) CUTTING (SUCCULENT)	1		
	2		
	3		
	4		
	5		
	6		
	7		
	8		
	9		
	10		
TOTAL			
MEAN			
D. 15 CM (6 IN) CUTTING (HARDENED)	1		
	2		
	3		
	4		
	5		
	6		
	7		
	8		
	9		
	10		
TOTAL			
MEAN			

DATA EVALUATION

1. Prepare bar graphs based on an evaluation of your data. In all cases plot the mean values for your treatments.

   A) Effect of size of cutting and type of wood on the mean visual ratings.

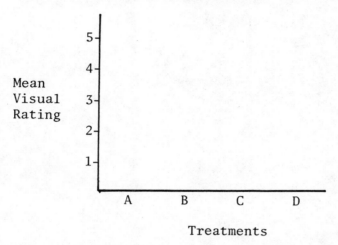

   B) Effect of size of cutting and type of wood on the mean number of roots.

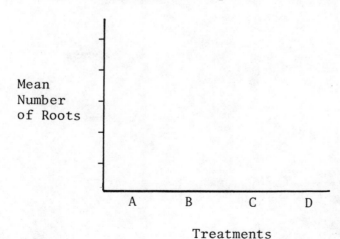

THOUGHT PROVOKERS

1. From an economic point of view what are the advantages of large cuttings?

2. In contrast to question 1, what do you feel are the advantages of small cuttings?

3. How does the type of wood from which the cutting has been prepared influence rooting?

4. Why would you expect the size of the cutting to be more important with deciduous hardwood cuttings?

Growth Regulators

There are apparently a number of organic compounds that may be present or absent in particular plants that may stimulate or inhibit the rooting process. Cuttings from some species root easily while those from other species may initiate roots with great difficulty or not at all. A number of compounds, which may be naturally occurring, can be applied to cuttings to encourage rooting.

The material often considered the best and most commonly used to stimulate rooting is IBA, or indolebutyric acid. IBA has weak auxin activity and is destroyed relatively slowly by auxin-destroying enzyme systems. In addition, IBA does not translocate readily and is retained near the area of application, thus further aiding root initiation.

2,4-dichlorophenoxyacetic acid (2,4-D) promotes rooting in numerous species, however, because it is readily translocated, it quite often tends to inhibit future shoot development. Numerous other phenoxy compounds including 2,4,5-T, 2,4,5-TP, 2,4,5-TB and 2,4-DB have proven to be effective rooting compounds without causing excessive plant injury, provided that they are used at extremely low concentrations. The major problem, however, in the usage of these compounds continues to be the narrow range of concentrations at which they can be used.

In addition to promoting roots, these growth regulators may also alter the type of root system produced, as well as the number of roots. IBA applications tend to produce strong, fibrous root systems, while 2,4-D and related compounds stimulate the production of bushy, stunted root systems with more or less thick, bent roots.

Another excellent growth regulator commonly used for root promotion is NAA, naphthaleneacetic acid. NAA is considered to be more toxic than IBA and excessive concentrations may cause inhibition of rooting and subsequent growth or both.

Both IBA and NAA are considered to be more effective in inducing root initiation than the naturally occurring IAA, indoleacetic acid. In addition, IAA is unstable and decomposition occurs very rapidly in unsterilized solutions. Also, strong sunlight can destroy a 10 ppm solution of IAA in 15 minutes.

APPLICATION OF ROOT PROMOTING SUBSTANCES

There are many methods for applying root promoting compounds. However, only the quick dip, the prolonged solution or dilute solution dip and powder or talc applications are in widespread commercial usage. Other methods of application such as the use of growth regulators incorporated into lanolin paste, and the insertion into the cutting of toothpicks soaked in auxin are not commercially used due to inconvenience.

QUICK DIP METHOD

In the quick dip method, the basal ends of the cutting are dipped for 5 to 15 seconds in a concentrated solution (500 to 10,000 ppm) of the growth regulator dissolved in an alcoholic solution (50:50 ethyl alcohol - distilled water). When using this method, the growth regulator is absorbed through the intact tissue, leaf scars, wounds and the basal end of the cutting. The cuttings are then placed in the rooting medium. The quick dip method has the principle advantage that less equipment is necessary for soaking than when using the prolonged soaking method. When using this method, the amount of growth regulator applied per unit area is constant and is not nearly as dependent on the external conditions surrounding the cuttings. In addition, the solution can be used repeatedly, but should always be tightly sealed between uses so the alcohol will not evaporate.

PROLONGED SOLUTION METHOD

The prolonged solution or dilute dip is an older method of applying growth regulators to the base of cuttings. The cuttings are usually allowed to remain in the dilute solution for a period of 12-24 hours prior to insertion into the rooting medium. The concentrations used with this method vary from 20-200 ppm depending upon the plant species to be rooted.

Cuttings treated in this manner are generally placed in a shaded location at a room temperature of approximately 20°C (68°F). Much more of the solution is absorbed when the cuttings are placed in warm, dry conditions where the transpiration rate will be accelerated. For this reason, it is best to place cuttings to be treated with a dilute solution in a moist, humid atmosphere during the soaking period, so a slower, more steady uptake of growth regulator is obtained. The amount required in a dilute solution will vary with the species treated, the time of year the cuttings are obtained and the growth regulator used.

POWDER OR TALC METHOD

This is the most widely used commercial method for the application of growth regulators to cuttings. In this method the base of the cuttings are treated with the growth regulator mixed with clay or more commonly a talcum powder carrier. Commercially prepared materials vary in concentration from 1,000 to 10,000 ppm. Homemade talc preparations can vary even more, depending upon the nature of the species to be propagated.

When treating cuttings with a talc preparation it is often desirable to make fresh cuts at the base of the cutting in order to insure greater absorption. The basal 2-3 cm (1 in) of the cutting is often moistened with water, and while still damp, placed into the powder. All excess talc is shaken from the cutting, leaving just a hint of the talc preparation, thus preventing possible toxic effects. The cuttings are stuck in the rooting bench immediately after treatment, with care being given to avoid rubbing off any of the adhering powder. (To achieve this, it is often necessary to use a knife or thick label to make a trench in the rooting medium prior to inserting the cuttings.)

It is advisable when using commercial talc preparations to place a small portion into a temporary container, rather than place the cuttings into the entire stock of powder thereby contaminating it with various forms of fungi and bacteria. When finished, the remaining material should be discarded rather than returned to the stock container.

PRECAUTIONS WITH GROWTH REGULATORS

The use of old solutions of the various growth regulators should be avoided, as they will more than likely produce negative results. Therefore, it is advisable to prepare just enough solution required for the job and then discard it. New mixtures are best if prepared from a stock solution just prior to use. Dilute solutions of IBA and NAA may lose their effectiveness within a few days. Growth regulator preparations in talc or similar carriers may retain their activity for several months or even years if tightly sealed, while concentrated solutions that are 50% or more alcohol retain their activity indefinitely.

SELECTED REFERENCE MATERIALS

Damanski, R., T. T. Kozlowski and S. Sasaki. 1969. Interactions of applied growth regulators and temperature on root initiation in Salix cuttings. J. Amer. Soc. Hort. Sci. 93:39-41.

Lanphear, F. O. and R. P. Meahl. 1963. Influence of endogenous rooting cofactors and environment on the seasonal fluctuation in root initiation of selected evergreen cuttings. Proc. Amer. Soc. Hort. Sci. 83:811-818.

Lee, C. I. 1969. The relationship between rooting cofactors of easy- and difficult-to-root cuttings of three clones of Rhododendron. Proc. Inter. Plant Prop. Soc. 19:391-398.

McGuire, J. J. 1967. Entrance of synthetic growth regulator IAA-2-14C into cuttings of Ilex crenata 'Convexa'. Proc. Inter. Plant Prop. Soc. 17:322-328.

McGuire, J. J., L. S. Albert and V. G. Shutak. 1969. Use of centrifugation to obtain auxin extracts from cuttings treated with terminal applications of 3-indoleacetic acid. J. Amer. Soc. Hort. Sci. 94:41-43.

Read, P. E. and V. C. Hoysler. 1969. Stimulation and retardation of adventitious root formation by application of B-nine and cycocel. J. Amer. Soc. Hort. Sci. 94:314-316.

Ryan, G. 1969. Etiolation as an aid in propagation. Proc. Inter. Plant Prop. Soc. 19:69-76.

NOTES

LABORATORY PROJECT XI. EVALUATION OF GROWTH REGULATOR CONCENTRATION ON ROOT INITIATION.

PURPOSE:
To illustrate the role growth regulators play when used at varying concentrations on the root initiation and root production process.

MATERIALS:
Chrysanthemum (C. morifolium) cuttings or similar easy to root materials
Propagation knife
Labels
Pencil
Auxins (use only one of the following for the complete experiment)
IAA, IBA, NAA
Beakers
Propagation medium in flats

PROCEDURE:
1. Print a label for each treatment - Treatments

            0 ppm - Control
     625 ppm
  1250 ppm
  2500 ppm
  5000 ppm

2. Select 25 uniform cuttings and divide them into 5 equal groups.
3. Recut the base of each cutting.
4. Dip the base of each group of cuttings into the proper solution concentration for 15 SECONDS.
5. Stick the cuttings into the flat of medium with the appropriate label in front.
6. Firm the medium around the base of the cuttings.
7. Place the propagation flat on the bench under mist.

RESULTS:
1. After 2 weeks carefully remove the rooted cuttings from the flat and wash the roots with water.
2. Evaluate the cuttings on a 1-5 visual rating scale. Record the results on the data summary sheet.
3. Evaluate the cuttings by counting the number of roots and record the results on the data summary sheet.

DATA SUMMARY

	CUTTING NUMBER	VISUAL RATING	NUMBER ROOTS		CUTTING NUMBER	VISUAL RATING	NUMBER ROOTS
0 PPM				**2500 PPM**			
	1				1		
	2				2		
	3				3		
	4				4		
	5				5		
	TOTAL				TOTAL		
	MEAN				MEAN		
625 PPM				**5000 PPM**			
	1				1		
	2				2		
	3				3		
	4				4		
	5				5		
	TOTAL				TOTAL		
	MEAN				MEAN		
1250 PPM							
	1						
	2						
	3						
	4						
	5						
	TOTAL						
	MEAN						

DATA EVALUATION

1. Prepare bar graphs based on the evaluation of your results from this experiment. Plot in this graph the mean values for the various treatments.

   A) Effect of varying growth regulator concentrations on the mean visual evaluation of the rooting response.

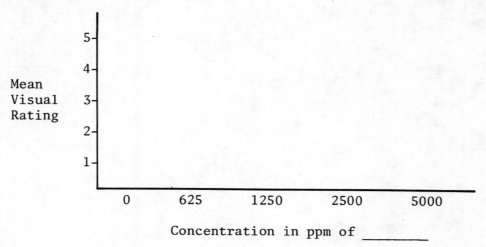

Mean Visual Rating

Concentration in ppm of _____

   B) Effect of varying growth regulator concentrations on the mean number of roots.

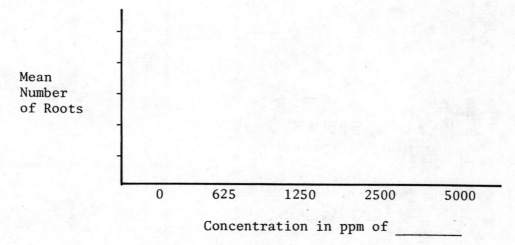

Mean Number of Roots

Concentration in ppm of _____

THOUGHT PROVOKERS

1. What inferences can be drawn from your observations of the effect of in-creased growth regulator concentration on the rooting response of the cuttings?

2. List 3 growth regulator materials used for increasing rooting responses of cuttings, including their structures and the concentration range at which they would normally be most effective on softwood cuttings.

3. List at least 3 additional materials that can also be used to promote rooting of cuttings.

4. What substances can be added to a rooting powder that can offer beneficial results in rooting?

5. What response, in addition to the inhibition of root development, might you expect to find if too high a concentration of growth regulator is used on softwood cuttings?

6. Discuss 2 disadvantages of a talc preparation of growth regulator as compared to the concentrated solution dip method of application.

ADDITIONAL THOUGHT PROVOKERS

1. Now that you are a commercial propagator, you have decided that you wish
    to treat some Juniperus horizontalis 'Hughes' cuttings with a dilute
    solution of IBA at a concentration of 175 ppm for 12 hours. How many
    milligrams of crystalline IBA would you need to dissolve in an alcohol:
    water solution to obtain 800 ml of the 175 ppm solution?

2. You wish to propagate some oakleaf hydrangea cuttings, and after reviewing
    the literature you find that a concentrated solution of IAA at 2500 ppm
    for 10 seconds, is recommended. How many grams of IAA will you need to
    weigh out and dissolve in a 50/50 alcohol:water solution in order to
    prepare 1.5 liters of this solution?

3. How many milligrams of IBA will you have to weigh out in order to prepare
    750 ml of a 1250 ppm solution, in order to treat some Taxus baccata
    cuttings?

LABORATORY PROJECT XII.   EVALUATION OF THE DURATION OF GROWTH REGULATOR
                          APPLICATION ON ROOT INITIATION.

The purpose of treating cuttings with growth regulators is to increase
the number of cuttings that form roots, to hasten the process of root initiation and to increase the uniformity and number of roots per cuttings. To this
end, there are a number of different methods of application, each having distinct advantages and disadvantages.

In addition, the length of time that the growth regulator remains in
contact with the base of the cutting can also have profound effects on rooting
and it is to this point that this experiment is directed.

PURPOSE:
    To evaluate the effect that an increase in the time or duration of
auxin application will have on the root initiation and development process.

MATERIALS:
    Chrysanthemum (C. morifolium) cuttings or similar easy to root material
    Propagation knife
    Labels
    Pencil
    2500 ppm IBA
    250 ml beaker
    Propagation medium in flats

PROCEDURE:
    1. Print a label for each treatment.
            Treatments
            0 sec - control
            2 sec
           15 sec
            1 min
            5 min
           10 min
    2. Select 30 uniform cuttings and divide them into 6 equal groups.
    3. Recut the base of each cutting.
    4. Dip the base of each group of cuttings into 2500 ppm IBA for the
       proper time period.
    5. Stick the cuttings into the propagation flat with the appropriate
       label.
    6. Firm the medium around the base of the cuttings.
    7. Place the propagation flat under mist.

RESULTS:
1. After 2 weeks carefully remove the rooted cuttings from the flat and wash the roots with water.
2. Evaluate the cuttings using a 1-5 visual rating scale. Record your results on the data summary sheet.
3. Evaluate the cuttings by counting the number of roots and record your results on the data summary sheet.

NOTES

DATA SUMMARY

	CUTTING NUMBER	VISUAL RATING	NUMBER ROOTS		CUTTING NUMBER	VISUAL RATING	NUMBER ROOTS

0 SECONDS

	CUTTING NUMBER	VISUAL RATING	NUMBER ROOTS
1			
2			
3			
4			
5			
TOTAL			
MEAN			

1 MINUTE

	CUTTING NUMBER	VISUAL RATING	NUMBER ROOTS
1			
2			
3			
4			
5			
TOTAL			
MEAN			

2 SECONDS

	CUTTING NUMBER	VISUAL RATING	NUMBER ROOTS
1			
2			
3			
4			
5			
TOTAL			
MEAN			

5 MINUTES

	CUTTING NUMBER	VISUAL RATING	NUMBER ROOTS
1			
2			
3			
4			
5			
TOTAL			
MEAN			

15 SECONDS

	CUTTING NUMBER	VISUAL RATING	NUMBER ROOTS
1			
2			
3			
4			
5			
TOTAL			
MEAN			

10 MINUTES

	CUTTING NUMBER	VISUAL RATING	NUMBER ROOTS
1			
2			
3			
4			
5			
TOTAL			
MEAN			

DATA EVALUATION

1. Prepare the following bar graphs based on the evaluation of your results
   from this experiment. Plot on this graph the mean values you obtained
   for the various growth regulator treatments.

   A) Effect of the duration of IBA on the mean visual rating of the rooting
      response.

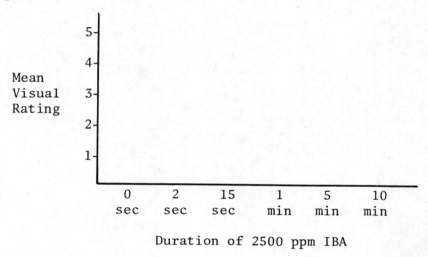

   Duration of 2500 ppm IBA

   B) Effect of the duration of IBA treatments on the mean number of roots.

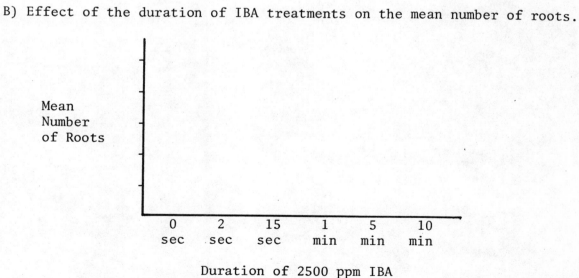

   Duration of 2500 ppm IBA

THOUGHT PROVOKERS

1. From the evaluation of your results, which of the treatments employed in this study gave the most outstanding results? Why didn't either longer or shorter treatments have similar results?

2. What inferences can be drawn from your observations of the effect of increased duration of growth regulator on the rooting response of the cuttings?

LABORATORY PROJECT XIII.   ROOTING OF CUTTINGS FROM FLOWERING AND VEGETATIVE
                           PLANTS.

PURPOSE:
    In horticultural practice it is widely recognized that cuttings from
flowering plants do not root as readily as those from vegetative plants. To
put this fact on a more practical basis, this experiment is designed to
compare the rooting capacity of flowering and vegetative plants. At the
conclusion of this experiment the student should have a greater insight into
the auxin-flowering relationship.

MATERIALS:
    Coleus (Coleus blumei) plants
        a) Flowering
        b) Vegetative
    Propagation knife
    Labels
    Pencil
    Propagation medium in flats

PROCEDURE:
    1. Print a label for each treatment.
                Treatments
        Flowering   Vegetative
         Node 1   Node 1
         Node 2   Node 2
         Node 3   Node 3
         Node 4   Node 4
         Node 5   Node 5
    2. Select enough shoots from both flowering and vegetative Coleus plants
       in order that you can prepare 5 cuttings from each of the above node
       positions.
    3. Cut the shoots just above the nodes into cuttings.
    4. Number each node starting with the apical bud as number 1.
    5. Stick the cuttings into the flat of medium with the appropriate label
       in front.
    6. Firm the medium around the base of the cuttings.
    7. Place the propagation flat under mist.

RESULTS:
    1. After 2 weeks carefully remove the rooted cuttings from the flat and
       wash the roots with water.
    2. Evaluate the cuttings on a 1-5 visual rating scale. Record the re-
       sults on the data summary sheet.
    3. Evaluate the cuttings by counting the number of roots per cutting.
       Record your results on the data summary sheet.

DATA SUMMARY - FLOWERING COLEUS

	CUTTING NUMBER	VISUAL RATING	NUMBER ROOTS		CUTTING NUMBER	VISUAL RATING	NUMBER ROOTS
NODE 1				**NODE 4**			
	1				1		
	2				2		
	3				3		
	4				4		
	5				5		
	TOTAL				TOTAL		
	MEAN				MEAN		
NODE 2				**NODE 5**			
	1				1		
	2				2		
	3				3		
	4				4		
	5				5		
	TOTAL				TOTAL		
	MEAN				MEAN		
NODE 3				**NODE 6**			
	1				1		
	2				2		
	3				3		
	4				4		
	5				5		
	TOTAL				TOTAL		
	MEAN				MEAN		

DATA SUMMARY - VEGETATIVE COLEUS

	CUTTING NUMBER	VISUAL RATING	NUMBER ROOTS		CUTTING NUMBER	VISUAL RATING	NUMBER ROOTS
NODE 1				**NODE 4**			
	1				1		
	2				2		
	3				3		
	4				4		
	5				5		
TOTAL				TOTAL			
MEAN				MEAN			
NODE 2				**NODE 5**			
	1				1		
	2				2		
	3				3		
	4				4		
	5				5		
TOTAL				TOTAL			
MEAN				MEAN			
NODE 3				**NODE 6**			
	1				1		
	2				2		
	3				3		
	4				4		
	5				5		
TOTAL				TOTAL			
MEAN				MEAN			

119

NOTES

DATA EVALUATION

1. Prepare bar graphs based on the evaluation of your results from this
    experiment. Plot in these graphs the mean values for the treatments
    obtained in your experiment.

    A) Visual evaluation of adventitious root production at subsequent nodal
       positions of vegetative and flower Coleus plants.

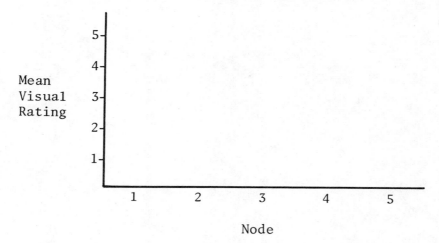

    B) Mean number of adventitious roots produced at subsequent nodal posi-
       tions from vegetative and flowering Coleus plants.

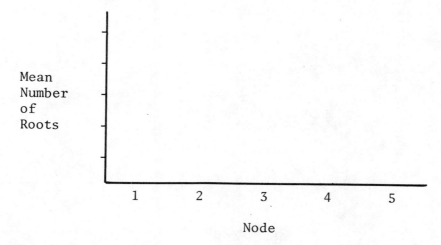

THOUGHT PROVOKERS

1. Explain the differences you observed in the rooting response between cuttings taken at the various nodes from the vegetative and flowering plants.

2. How might leaf area (i.e., size) have influenced these results?

LABORATORY PROJECT XIV.   EVALUATION OF APICAL, MEDIAL AND BASAL HARDWOOD
CUTTINGS.

Dividing the long shoots of some woody plants into several cuttings is a common practice used by many commercial plant propagators. When cuttings from the apical, medial and basal portions of these shoots are examined individually, there can be a distinct difference in their rooting response.

While it might be expected that the basal cuttings would display the best rooting, this is not always the case for all woody plants. Several factors are present that may affect the final results, including the movement of auxin, the number of preformed root initials and the level of carbohydrates present in the tissue.

PURPOSE:
To determine if position along a shoot has any effect on the rooting response of cuttings.

MATERIALS:
Hardwood cuttings of Red Osier Dogwood (Cornus sericea)
Propagation knife
Labels
Pencil
Rooting hormone
Propagation medium in flats

PROCEDURE:
1. Print a label for each treatment.
        Treatments
          Apical
          Medial
          Basal
2. Collect 10 hardwood cuttings approximately 10 cm (4 in) in length from the previous year's growth.
3. Cut the shoots into three equal portions carefully noting the proper polarity.
4. Replace a small amount of the rooting powder in a paper cup. (Never return the used hormone powder to the original container.)
5. Dip the base of each cutting into the rooting hormone and shake off the excess powder.
6. Stick the cuttings into the rooting medium in the propagation flat with the appropriate label.
7. Firm the medium around the base of the cuttings.
8. Place the propagation flat under mist.

RESULTS:
1. After 7-8 weeks carefully remove the rooted cuttings from the flat and wash the roots with water.
2. Evaluate the cuttings on a 1-5 visual rating scale. Record your results on the data summary sheet.
3. Evaluate the cuttings in terms of the number of roots formed per cutting. Record your results on the data summary sheet.

NOTES

DATA SUMMARY

	CUTTING NUMBER	VISUAL RATING	NUMBER ROOTS
APICAL	1		
	2		
	3		
	4		
	5		
	6		
	7		
	8		
	9		
	10		
TOTAL			
MEAN			
MEDIAL	1		
	2		
	3		
	4		
	5		
	6		
	7		
	8		
	9		
	10		
TOTAL			
MEAN			
BASAL	1		
	2		
	3		
	4		
	5		
	6		
	7		
	8		
	9		
	10		
TOTAL			
MEAN			

DATA EVALUATION

1. Prepare bar graphs based on an evaluation of your results from this experiment. Plot the mean treatment values for the 3 treatments in the bar graph below.

   A) Comparison of apical, medial and basal hardwood cuttings on the production of adventitious roots.

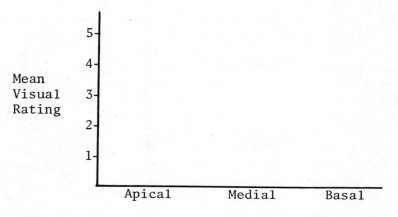

Portion of Wood

   B) Effect of apical, medial and basal hardwood cuttings on the number of adventitious roots produced.

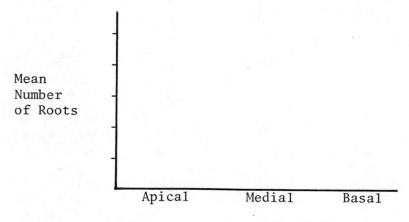

Portion of Wood

THOUGHT PROVOKERS

1. Based on your results, cuttings from what portion of the shoot produced the best root system? Why? Explain your results.

2. How would the movement of auxin affect the rooting response if it were the only contributing factor?

3. What are preformed root initials?

LABORATORY PROJECT XV. WOUNDING CUTTINGS.

Basal wounding is used on stem cuttings of woody plant materials in order
to stimulate root production. This procedure is used with such species as
junipers, arborvitae, rhododendron, and holly in order to increase root
production. With narrowleaf evergreens such as juniper, wounding may be
achieved simply by removing the lower leaves prior to sticking in the bench.
With deciduous or broadleaf evergreen materials, wounds are made with a
vertical cut on one or both sides of the base of the cutting for a distance
of 2-5 cm (1-2 in). The wound should penetrate through the bark and into the
wood tissue (Figure 21).

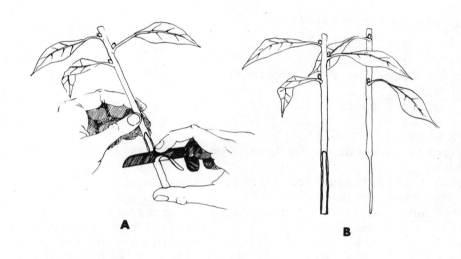

FIGURE 21. WOUNDING CUTTINGS.

In order to achieve the greatest benefit from wounding, treatment with
a root-promoting material is essential. Wounding has been noted to stimulate
heavier callus production and root formation along the margins of the wound.
It appears that the wounded tissues are stimulated to produce more root
primordia and ultimately more roots. This is believed due to a natural
accumulation of auxins and carbohydrate materials in the wounded area. In
addition, it has been suggested that these wounded tissues promote increased
ethylene production which is thought to enhance adventitious root formation.

Not only is root promotion enhanced following wounding, but wounded cuttings absorb more water from the surrounding propagation medium than comparable
unwounded cuttings. Similarly wounding of cuttings known to have a ring of

sclerenchyma cells in the cortex external to the region of origin of adventitious roots will often aid in allowing the roots to penetrate this band of cells.

PURPOSE:
To determine if wounding has any effect on the rooting response of cuttings.

MATERIALS:
Semi-hardwood cuttings of Royal Beauty cotoneaster (Cotoneaster dammeri 'Royal Beauty'), Cranberry cotoneaster (Cotoneaster apiculata), Manhattan euonymus (Euonymus patens 'Manhattan') or other suitable materials
Propagation knife
Labels
Pencil
Growth regulator
Paper cup
Propagation medium in flats

PROCEDURE:
1. Print a label for each treatment.
   Treatments
   0 wound - control
   1 wound
   2 wounds
2. Collect 5 hardwood or semi-hardwood cuttings 10-15 cm (4-6 in) in length.
3. Divide the cuttings into 3 equal groups.
4. Perform the treatments.
   0 wound - Control - no wounding is necessary.
   1 wound - Make a 2-3 cm (1 in) vertical cut, stripping the bark down one side of each cutting in one group.
   2 wounds - Similarly wound both sides of each cutting in another group.
5. Pour a small amount of the rooting hormone into a paper cup. (Never return the used powder to the original container.)
6. Dip the base, including the wounded area of each cutting into the rooting hormone and shake off the excess powder.
7. Stick the cuttings into the propagation flat with the appropriate label.
8. Firm the medium around the base of the cuttings.
9. Place the propagation flat under mist.

RESULTS:
1. After 7-8 weeks carefully remove the rooted cuttings from the flat and wash the roots with water.
2. Evaluate the cuttings on a 1-5 visual rating scale. Record your results on the data summary sheet.
3. Evaluate the cuttings by counting the number of roots formed per cutting. Record your results on the data summary sheet.

DATA SUMMARY

	CUTTING NUMBER	VISUAL RATING	NUMBER ROOTS
0 WOUND - CONTROL			
	1		
	2		
	3		
	4		
	5		
	TOTAL		
	MEAN		
1 WOUND			
	1		
	2		
	3		
	4		
	5		
	TOTAL		
	MEAN		
2 WOUNDS			
	1		
	2		
	3		
	4		
	5		
	TOTAL		
	MEAN		

NOTES

NAME _____

LAB SECTION _____

DATA EVALUATION

1. Prepare bar graphs based on the evaluation of your results from this experiment. Plot the mean treatment values for the various treatments in the bar graph below.

A) Effect of wounding on the mean visual evaluation of rooting.

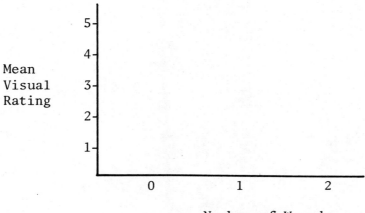

B) Effect of wounding on the mean number of roots initiated.

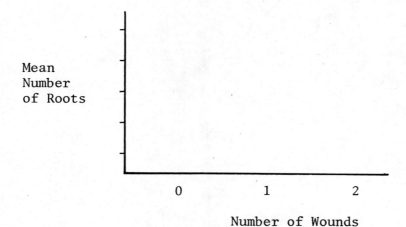

137

THOUGHT PROVOKERS

1. Why and to what extent is the process of wounding used in plant propagation?

2. From an evaluation of your results using the various wounding treatments, which treatment gave the best rooting response and why?

3. From what tissues does callus originate and does this tissue promote and/or retard root development?

4. Would you as an accomplished plant propagator recommend a wounding treatment for easily-rooted plant materials such as geraniums? Explain.

5. How would you explain to a group of nurserymen that wounding seems to improve the rooting response of many woody ornamentals?

LABORATORY PROJECT XVI.   EVALUATION OF THE INFLUENCE OF POLARITY ON ROOT
DEVELOPMENT OF CUTTINGS.

Polarity in the rooting of cuttings can be dramatically demonstrated. Stem cuttings will form roots at the proximal end or that end of the cutting which was nearest the crown and shoots at the distal end or that end nearest the shoot tip. When working with root cuttings, roots will form at the distal end and the new shoot will arise from the proximal end. If one attempts to change the position of the cuttings with respect to gravity, it will not alter this development of roots and shoots.

PURPOSE:

To demonstrate the effect of polarity on the development of roots on stem cuttings.

MATERIALS:

English ivy (Hedera helix) or Red Osier Dogwood (Cornus sericea) stem
    cuttings
Propagation knife
Labels
Propagation medium in flats
Growth regulator
Pencil
Paper cup

PROCEDURE:
1. Prepare a proper label for each of the following treatments.
    Treatments
    A. Not inverted (upright)
    B. Inverted with buds
    C. Inverted with buds removed
    D. Girdled (upright)
2. Prepare 10 cuttings for each treatment, approximately 10-13 cm (4-5
   in) in length.
3. Treat the cuttings with a rooting powder and stick into a propagation
   flat with the appropriate label.
4. Firm the medium around the base of the cuttings.
5. Place the propagation flat under mist.
6. Inspect the cuttings on a regular basis.

RESULTS:
1. After 4 weeks remove the cuttings from the flat and wash the roots
   with water to remove adhering soil particles.
2. Evaluate the cuttings on a 1-5 visual rating scale and record your
   results on the data summary sheet.
3. Evaluate the cuttings by counting the number of roots developed per
   cutting and record the results on the data summary sheet.

141

DATA SUMMARY

	CUTTING NUMBER	VISUAL RATING	NUMBER ROOTS		CUTTING NUMBER	VISUAL RATING	NUMBER ROOTS
TREATMENT A **NOT INVERTED**				**TREATMENT B** **INVERTED (WITH BUDS)**			
	1				1		
	2				2		
	3				3		
	4				4		
	5				5		
	6				6		
	7				7		
	8				8		
	9				9		
	10				10		
TOTAL				TOTAL			
MEAN				MEAN			
TREATMENT C **INVERTED (WITH BUDS REMOVED)**				**TREATMENT D** **GIRDLED (UPRIGHT)**			
	1				1		
	2				2		
	3				3		
	4				4		
	5				5		
	6				6		
	7				7		
	8				8		
	9				9		
	10				10		
TOTAL				TOTAL			
MEAN				MEAN			

DATA EVALUATION

1. Prepare bar graphs based on an evaluation of your results from this experiment. Plot the mean values for the treatments in the graphs.

   A) Effect of polarity on the mean visual evaluation of the rooting response.

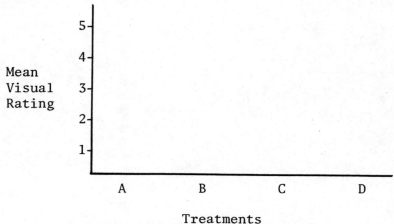

   B) Effect of polarity on the mean number of roots produced.

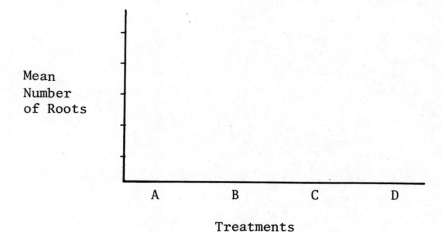

THOUGHT PROVOKERS

1. What is the significance of the girdle?

2. Why will some of the inverted cuttings survive?

3. What is meant by polarity? Could the knowledge obtained in this experiment actually be of beneficial importance to a grower rooting large quantities of plants?

LABORATORY PROJECT XVII.   PREPARATION OF ROOT CUTTINGS.

PURPOSE:
   To demonstrate the technique of propagation by root cuttings.

MATERIALS:
      Blackberry or Raspberry (Rubus sp.)
      Firethorn (Pyracantha sp.)
      Apple (Malus sp.), or Horseradish (Armoracia lapathifolia)
      Propagation medium in flats
      Potting medium
      Propagation knife
      Pruning shears
      Labels
      Pencil

PROCEDURE:
   1. Dry the proper plants and remove the soil adhering to the roots by
      gently shaking.
   2. Select roots 6-12 mm (1/4-1/2 in) in diameter and cut into pieces
      5-10 cm (2-4 in) long.
   3. Sow the root pieces horizontally on the medium surface. (If the root
      pieces are placed vertically in the medium, be sure to retain the
      proper polarity.)
   4. Cover the root pieces with 2.5-5 cm (1-2 in) of medium.
   5. Water the flats and place them in the greenhouse.

RESULTS:
   1. Observe the growth of the root pieces periodically during the next
      several months. Watch for the development of the new shoots.
   2. Carefully remove one of the newly developed plants and note where
      the new shoots have developed.

NOTES

THOUGHT PROVOKERS

1. What type of buds develop on root cuttings? From what tissue do these buds usually arise?

2. Why must the proper polarity of the root pieces be maintained if they are planted in a vertical fashion?

3. Why do plants such as thornless raspberries become thorny if propagated by root cuttings?

Ferns

Ferns have been growing on the earth for millions of years and are generally considered to be among the first plants (after mosses and algae) to have evolved after the earth was formed. Although they are not used in gardens today to a great extent, ferns are useful in the landscape. In addition, ferns are important in the wholesale and retail florist business for use as pot plants and cut fronds.

The life cycle of the fern (Figure 22) differs from higher plants and begins when the haploid (1N) spores, which are borne on the underside of the fronds (leaves) in sacs or clusters called sporangia (several sporangia are clustered together in a sori), fall to the ground and initiate growth. If the spore remains sufficiently moist, it germinates and develops into a haploid (1N), many celled, heartshaped organ called a prothallus which, when fully developed, is 6 to 12 mm (0.25 to 0.50 in) in diameter.

The prothallus develops root-like structures, rhizoids, which absorb water and nutrients from the soil. In time, as the prothallus matures, the male (antheridium) and the female (archegonium) organs are formed on the underside surface. When the antheridium matures, sperm cells (1N) are produced and, in the presence of water, are transported to the archegonium where fusion with an egg (1N) cell results in the formation of a diploid (2N) zygote (Figure 22).

The zygote, or young sporophytic plant, develops on the prothallus. Initially, a foot or root-like structure develops, through which water and nutrients are absorbed from the prothallus, and eventually a root develops. At the same time, a primary leaf and stem begin to develop. Ultimately the stem develops into a rhizome from which the fronds and permanent root develop.

Ferns are typically propagated by spores, division and, in a few cases, by the removal and growing of bulblets which form on the fronds. To grow ferns from spores, collect fronds when the sporangia are ripe, but not empty (examine with a hand lens), and place in an envelope to dry at 21-24°C (70-75 °F) for a week. When the spores have been discharged, sow in pots of sterilized soil by carefully sprinkling on the soil surface. An extremely thin layer of sphagnum peat should be gently sifted over the soil. Set the pots in a pan of water (preferably distilled, in order to prevent salt damage) in order to moisten the soil by capillary action. Never water from the top since this will wash the spores to a depth that will prevent their germination. Once the soil surface is moist, remove the pots and place in a warm environment, 18-24°C (65-75°F). Cover the pots with a pane of glass or polyethylene to retain the moisture in the soil. If water is required, use capillary water from the bottom or a very fine spray over the top.

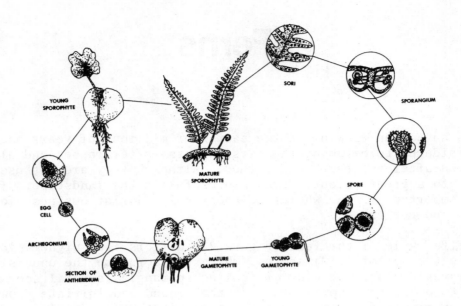

FIGURE 22. LIFE CYCLE OF THE FERN.

The spores will begin to germinate in 3 to 4 days, although some species may take longer. A good indication that the spores are growing is a greenish cast to the soil surface. The prothallia are usually fully grown in about 3 months. At this time, they should be frequently sprayed or misted with water so that fertilization will take place. Once the new sporophyte begins to develop, it usually takes a period of 1 to 2 years before the plants are commercially large enough to be sold. During the period of sporophytic development, damping-off can become a serious problem and occassional applications of a general purpose fungicide may be warranted.

Ferns can usually be divided at any time of the year. However, this is commonly done in the spring just before the new flush of growth begins. The plant is removed from the ground or pot and the soil is shaken from the root mass. The root mass is gently pulled apart so that the rhizomes, each with several fronds and roots, are separated from one another. In some cases, it may be necessary to divide the crown by cutting the clump of rhizomes into several smaller pieces. The pieces are then repotted.

Several ferns, in particular the Bulblet Bladder-Fern (Cystopteris bulbifera) form small bulblets about the size of a garden pea on the underside of the fronds. When mature, the bulblets can be planted and will produce, within 2 years, a fern plant similar to the parent plant.

SELECTED REFERENCE MATERIAL

Fliflet, T. Growing ferns from spores. Amer. Fern J. 51(3):113-127.

Roberts, D. J. 1965. Modern propagation of ferns. Proc. Inter. Plant Prop. Soc. 15:317-322.

NOTES

154

LABORATORY PROJECT XVIII.   PROPAGATION OF FERNS BY SPORES.

PURPOSE:
   To demonstrate the technique of propagating ferns from haploid (1N) spores.

MATERIALS:
   Bird's-Nest Fern (Asplenium nidus), Brake Fern (Pteris sp.), Maidenhair
      Fern (Adiantum sp.), Hares-Foot Fern (Polypodium aureum) or other
      suitable material
   Envelopes
   Knife or scissors
   Pots
   Potting medium
   Glass panes or polyethylene
   Labels
   Pencil

PROCEDURE:
   1. Print a label for each lot of fern spores to be sown.
   2. Collection of fern spores:
      A. Collect fern fronds with mature unopened sori and place in an
         envelope.
      B. Dry the cut fern fronds for 1 week at 21-24°C (70-75°F).
      C. When dry, tap the envelope sharply to dislodge the remaining
         spores from the sori.
      D. Remove the frond from the envelope and discard.
   3. Uniformly broadcast the spores over the medium surface.
   4. Cover the pot with a glass pane or piece of polyethylene and place in
      the tray of distilled water in order to wet the medium.
   5. After the medium surface is wet, place the pot in a warm, moderately
      lighted location (preferably a fluorescent light box).

RESULTS:
   1. Observe the growth of the spores, prothallus and new sporophytic
      generation.

NOTES

THOUGHT PROVOKERS

1. Discuss how fern spores differ from the seeds of flowering plants.

2. Describe how spores are produced by the fern plant.

Grafting

There are several grafting techniques which are successfully used in both nursery and orchard practice with which every horticulturist should be familiar. The grafting technique to be used will depend upon the conditions under which the grafting is to be done. Whip and tongue grafting, sometimes referred to as whip grafting or bench grafting, is the most common grafting method used for fruit trees.

Cleft grafting is the technique most frequently used in top working fruit crops, while other techniques that are used at times include bark grafting and side grafting. In the broadest sense, these may both be considered as variations of cleft and whip and tongue grafting.

Whatever the grafting technique selected, it is necessary to place the cambial tissues of the stock and that of the scion in close promixity to one another. The stock and scion must line up in the same direction, and when this is done with 2 compatible cultivars, and the scion is held firmly in place without drying out before healing takes place, the unions should be successful.

WHIP AND TONGUE GRAFTING

The whip and tongue method works best when the stock and scion are of a similar diameter, generally between 0.5 and 1.0 cm (0.25-0.38 in). In general, seedlings, rooted layers or cuttings are whip grafted in late winter or early spring after they have been dug from the nursery row. When this type grafting is done indoors, it is commonly referred to as bench grafting.

The whip and tongue graft (Figure 23) can be mastered with practice if performed as follows. Cut the scion from the mid-portion of a dormant shoot, so that it has 2 or more good healthy buds. Begin by making a sloping cut at the base of the scion from 2.5 to 4.0 cm (1-1.5 in) long (Figure 23 A & B). The longer the scion, the longer the cut will need to be. In the sloping cut surface, about 1/3 the distance from the tip, begin a second cut nearly parallel to the first, making it 1 to 2 cm (0.5-0.75 in) long (Figure 23 C).

Next prepare the end of the stock to be grafted in the same manner as the scion (Figure 23 D, E & F). Fit the stock and scion together tightly so that the cambiums of the cut surfaces match (as closely as possible) or are in near proximity to one another (Figure 23 G). If the stock and scion are of equal diameters, both sides should match; however, if they are of unequal size, make sure that one of the cut surfaces matches as closely as is possible.

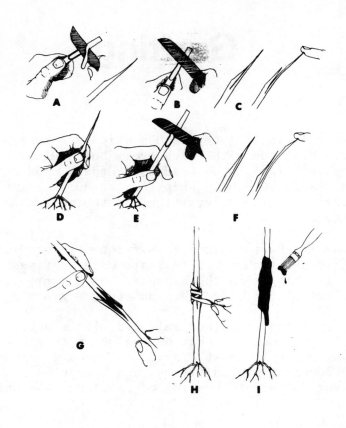

FIGURE 23.   WHIP AND TONGUE GRAFTING.

Tie the graft firmly by wrapping it with a budding rubber strip, grafting adhesive tape or other similar material (Figure 23 H & I).   If the wrapping material does not decay and break as growing takes place, it should be cut about 1 month after growth begins.   Wax the graft unions completely to prevent the tissues from drying.   In addition, it is also beneficial to wax the tips of the scions.

CLEFT GRAFTING
The cleft graft is the most widely used method in the U.S. for topworking fruit trees.   This graft is made by inserting a scion into a carefully made split in the stub of a scaffold branch or in the case of a small tree, the trunk.   Such grafts are commonly made on stocks that are between 2.5 and 5.0 cm (1-2 in) in diameter.   The cleft graft is commonly done in late winter or early spring.   Results are generally best when the cleft graft is done just before the spring growth begins, but dormant scions must be used.

The cleft grafting procedure is fairly simple, but does require a special cleft grafting tool in order to do it properly and efficiently.

To begin the cleft graft, saw off the trunk or scaffold branch, then split carefully with the cleft grafting tool and mallet (Figure 24 A & B). The split should be across the center of the stub and extend downward 4 to 5 cm (1.5-2 in), depending on the size of the stock and scion being used. The split or cleft, is opened with the chisel end of the grafting tool so that the scion can be inserted easily. Stocks in excess of 5 cm (2 in) usually have a scion placed at each end of the split.

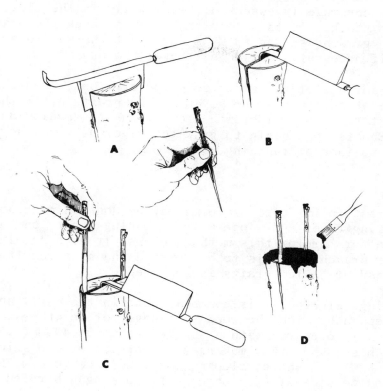

FIGURE 24.   CLEFT GRAFTING.

Prepare the scion in the shape of a wedge at the basal end. One side of the wedge should be slightly narrower than the other. Each cut should be made about 4 cm (1.5 in) long with a single stroke of the propagation knife and tapered evenly towards the end. If the scion is not made in this manner, it will make contact with the stock only at the thickest portion. The other end of the scion is cut off so that 2 or 3 buds remain above the wedge cuts.

Insert the scion in the side of the opened cleft of the stock, with a gentle push towards the center (Figure 24 C). Push it gently into position so that the scion cambium matches the stock cambium. If a small scion is placed in a large stock, the matching is not done as easily since the thickness of the bark tissues will vary considerably between the stock and scion. If necessary, slant the scion slightly so that the cambium will contact at least a part of the stock cambium. Larger stocks will take 2 scions. If this is done, the point of contact should begin about 0.6 cm (0.25 in) below the shoulder of the stock. Once the scion is in place, remove the grafting tool. The pressure of the stock will hold it in position.

Coat all surfaces including the scion tips with grafting wax (Figure 24 D). Complete coverage is essential, especially in the cleft graft and on the sides of the stock. It is a good practice to check the grafts periodically during the growing season to make sure that the wax covering remains intact. Rewax if necessary, but do not cover the buds.

If the cut surface of the stock or scion drys out, then the union will not occur. Some attention must be given to the grafts after they begin to grow. It is best to allow all growth from scions to develop during the first season. Shoots that begin to grow too vigorously may be pinched back in early summer to induce branching.

BARK GRAFTING
The bark graft in its various forms may be done in place of the cleft graft in topworking trees and especially in making grafts on large diameter stubs. Many grafters prefer this method because it does not involve splitting the stub or branch which is to be grafted and as a result a higher percentage of "takes" or healed grafts is achieved.

Bark grafting (Figure 25) is commonly done in the early spring at a time when the bark separates from the wood with ease, or in other words is "slipping". The scion is prepared with a single cut about 4 cm (1.5 in) long on one side of the basal end, thus making this portion of the scion wedge shaped (Figure 25 A, B & C). A short, sloping cut 1 to 2 cm (0.5-0.75 in) long, is made on the opposite side of the longer cut, forming a beveled end on the scion. A shoulder is cut at the upper end of the longer cut, so the scion will fit over the top of the stock stub.

The branch or trunk is cut off as in cleft grafting, then a section of bark is removed from the top of the stub, with the exact dimensions of the beveled end of the scion (Figure 25 D). The prepared scion is held in place on the outside of the bark. With a sharp knife, the bark is cut to correspond with the length and width of the wedge-shaped end of the scion (Figure 25 E). The lower end of the scion with the long bevel towards the stock, is then pushed under the bark between the 2 cuts, thus separating the bark from the wood, as the scion is pushed downward (Figure 25 F). The lifted bark is then cut off even with the top of the short bevel on the outside of the scion. The scion is tacked with 2 small brads or nails to hold it firmly to the stock (Figure 25 G). All cut surfaces of the graft union should be thoroughly waxed, as well as the tip of the scion (Figure 25 H).

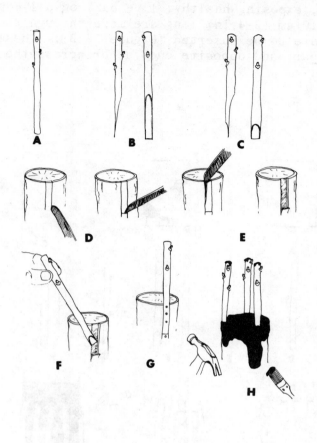

FIGURE 25.   BARK GRAFTING.

If the stock is large enough, additional scions can be placed in a single stub.   These should be spaced 5 to 10 cm (2-4 in) apart.   In addition, it should be noted that there are many variations to bark grafting.   Some graf- ters prefer to leave the stock bark intact and tacking it with the scion to the stock.   There are also variations in shaping the bevel end of the scion.

BRIDGE GRAFTING

Bridge grafting is primarily used to "bridge-over" a dead or wounded area on a tree trunk or main scaffold branch.   It is frequently used to re- pair trees damaged by mice or rabbits feeding on the base of the trunk and lower branches of young trees.   Apple and pear trees can be effectively bridge grafted.

Bridge grafting can be done easily when the bark slips, which is usually after spring growth begins.   It may be done anytime up to bloom or even later, providing dormant scions are available.   The procedure is rather time-consum- ing and some practice is necessary in order to develop the skills that lead to successful bridge grafts.

163

In preparing the area to be bridged over, carefully remove all dead and injured bark tissue, exposing healthy, live bark on all edges (Figure 26 A). Vertical cuts 5 to 10 cm (2-4 in) long are made through the bark where the ends of the scions are to be inserted (Figure 26 B). These cuts are spaced about 5 cm (2 in) apart and opposite each other across the injured area (Figure 26 C).

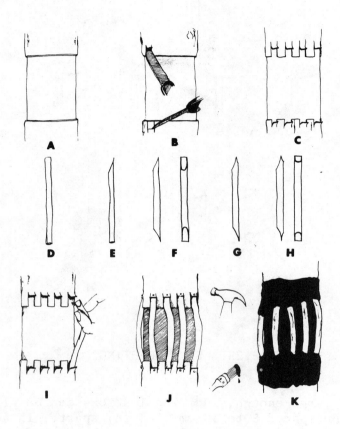

FIGURE 26.   BRIDGE GRAFTING

Dormant water sprouts of <u>suitable</u> lengths make <u>suitable</u> scions.   Each sprout is cut so that it is slightly longer than the distance between the extremities of the two bark cuts opposite each other.   Each end is then shaped into a wedge with beveled points, in the same manner as described for bark grafting, except that the shoulder is omitted (Figure 26 D-H).

The bark along one of the slits is gently lifted with a knife blade or sharpened stick, the end of the scion slid under the bark and into place with the cut surface adjacent to the wood of the tree (Figure 26 I).   The same procedure is followed with the other end of the scion, then both ends are tacked down with one or two small brads (Figure 26 J).   Since the scion was slightly longer than the area bridged, it will have a slight bow.   This puts tension on the ends of the scion, helping to hold it in place. Scions are spaced about 5 cm (2 in) apart. When all the scions needed to bridge the area are in place, the graft unions and all exposed surfaces are covered with a coat of wax or asphalt compound (Figure 26 K).

As in bark grafting, there are also variations in the bridge grafting technique. Shaping of the beveled ends of the scions may be varied, especially to fit different types of cuts in the bark on the tree being grafted. In the case of mature trees, and bark which does not slip easily, it may be necessary to cut a section of bark completely from the area where the scion is to fit. This must be done carefully so the beveled surface of the scion fits snugly into the area from which the bark was removed. The scions are tacked in as previously described.

If buds on the inserted scions begin to grow during the first year, the young shoots should be rubbed off as soon as noticed. If growth is permitted to continue, the graft unions may be weakened or even fail completely. Since young bridge grafts are subject to rodent injury, they should be protected with hardward cloth, aluminum foil, or other suitable coverings as soon as the grafting is completed.

INARCHING

Occasionally, extensive injury to the lower trunk and root system occurs, making the wounded area unsatisfactory for bridge grafting. In such cases the process of inarching the ends of trunks or branches of seedling trees or suckers of the injured tree into the live bark area above the injury of the trunk can bring about satisfactory tree recovery (Figure 27). As with bridge grafting, this method is successful with apple and pear.

One year old seedlings are planted around the tree and as close to the trunk as possible. In planting, the young trees should be slanted towards the trunk of the injured tree. The seedlings should be spaced 15 to 30 cm (6-8 in) apart around the tree, using a sufficient number to bridge over the injured area properly.

Dead and injured bark is first cut away from the injured trunk, exposing healthy bark tissues. The ends of the seedlings then may be prepared and inserted beneath the tree bark in the same way as in bridge grafting. If necessary to bridge-over an extended dead area, the end of the seedling may be bark grafted to the trunk or main scaffold branch higher up on the tree. The technique is the same as bark grafting. Such grafts should be protected from rodent injury as in the case of bridge grafting.

GRAFTING TOOLS

The tools and equipment normally used in budding and grafting can be purchased from garden and orchard supply stores, or from nurseries and special dealers. The essential tools are pruning shears, knives, saws, cleft grafting tool, mallet or suitable hammer, sharpening stones, and a supply of No. 18 brads for bridge grafting.

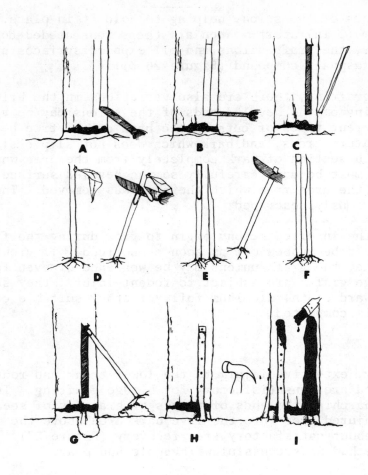

FIGURE 27.   INARCHING.

The grafting tool (clefter) used in cleft grafting can be made in the
farm workshop by shaping a hard piece of steel to the shape illustrated in
Figure 24. The appropriate edges are then sharpened. The cutting edge may
be either straight or concave. A concave cutting edge makes smooth edges for
receiving the scions by cutting the bark before the wood can split and tear
the bark away. Most tools used in cleft grafting have straight edges and
when used carefully will split the branch little beyond the desired limit.

When hard waxes are used for coating graft unions, a heater is needed
to melt the wax and keep it thin enough for application. A small unit equipped with an alcohol burner is adequate.

Budding and grafting knives should be made of good steel and kept razor
sharp at all times. A dull knife can be the cause of poor healing and poor
union of scion with stock. A grafting knife should have a straight-edged
blade; a budding knife with the edge curving upward at the point works best.
It is the sharp curved end of the blade that is used most to cut the bark
for insertion of the buds.

GRAFTING WAX

All grafting wounds, except buddings, need to be covered with a protective coating immediately after completion of the graft. Characteristics of a suitable grafting wax or other protective coating are:

1. Retains the moisture in the wood and excludes air and fungi from the wounds.
2. Contains no material that would injure live tissue in the strength recommended for use.
3. Has sufficient body to fill cracks easily and is convenient to handle.
4. Is elastic enough to accommodate itself to changes in dimension of stock and scion resulting from growth.
5. Neither cracks in cold weather nor runs in hot weather.
6. Is relatively inexpensive.

For those who wish to prepare their own grafting waxes, the following formula and information are presented.

A standard brush wax consists of the following ingredients: resin - 5 parts, beeswax - 1 part, linseed oil - 1/4 part, lampblack or powdered charcoal.

First, slowly melt the resin then add the beeswax. When both are completely melted add the linseed oil and stir. When mixed well, remove from the heat and add the lampblack or powdered charcoal a little at a time while stirring slowly. Continue stirring until it has a smooth consistency and is a uniform black color. The lampblack or charcoal will make the wax tougher and more pliable. Before use, the wax must be melted to a consistency that can be brushed on easily, yet cools quickly and will not run.

Any wound coating should be inspected periodically to make sure it is still intact. If it has broken away or "chipped" badly before healing is complete, a new coating should be applied over the old one. Brushes, tools, or hands soiled with asphalt-water type graft dressings may be easily cleaned with gasoline or kerosene before washing with soap and water.

STOCK AND SCION SELECTION

The selection of stock and scion material varies with the plant species and cultivar. For deciduous species, where grafting is commonly performed in late winter or early spring, use scion material from the previous season's growth. In general, 1 year old wood is preferable, however, 2 or 3 year old wood can be used. It has been reported that with Fagus sylvatica, 2 and 3 year old wood gave the best grafting results.

The usual recommendation is to select wood from moderately vigorous shoots, and to use the lower or middle two-thirds of wood 1 year old. Some grafters prefer to use terminals, but this portion may be less well matured and much lower in stored carbohydrates, making it unsuitable for grafting. Scion wood of deciduous species should be collected while dormant and stored under refrigerated conditions at temperatures between 1 and 4°C (33-40°F).

This wood should be collected when temperatures are above freezing and from healthy, virus-free trees. After being cut to suitable lengths, bundled and labeled as to cultivar, the scions should be packed in slightly moistened peat or sawdust and wrapped in polyethylene sheets or bags. If kept too moist, the scions may mold, thus becoming useless. On the other hand, storage at temperatures below freezing can result in damage to the scion wood.

When working with coniferous evergreens, it is generally considered essential to have the stocks well established in pots. Numerous individuals have reported that for pines and spruce the stocks should be potted for nearly a year prior to the actual grafting operation. Juniperus on the other hand, can be grafted bare rooted.

Broadleaf evergreens such as camellia, rhododendron and holly are usually grafted in late winter or early spring before growth starts. With rhododendrons, it has been suggested that some cultivars can not be dormant winter grafted. Scions with partially hardened wood and fully developed leaves obtained between mid-June and mid-July gave excellent results. In addition, certain subtropical fruit and nut crops such as the avocado, litchi, and macadamia can be grafted at almost any time of the year.

SELECTED REFERENCE MATERIAL

Alley, C. J. 1960. Machine grafting and pre-planting techniques for grape bench grafts. Proc. Inter. Plant Prop. Soc. 10:239-246.

Banta, E. S. 1967. Fruit tree propagation. Ohio Coop. Ext. Service Bull. 481.

Carville, L. L. 1970. Environmental control for grafting. Proc. Inter. Plant Prop. Soc. 20:232-238.

Copes, D. 1969. External detection of incompatible Douglas-fir grafts. Proc. Inter. Plant Prop. Soc. 19:97-102.

DeGroot, C. 1960. Successful winter grafting of Juniper varieties on un-rooted cuttings. Proc. Inter. Plant Prop. Soc. 10:124-127.

Garner, R. J. 1968. The Grafters Handbook, 3rd Edition. Faber and Faber, London.

Hasek, R. E. 1968. Some scion-stock interrelations. Proc. Inter. Plant Prop. Soc. 18:133-136.

Holmes, K. D. 1966. Storage of rooted cuttings, unrooted cuttings, scions and budwood. Proc. Inter. Plant Prop. Soc. 16:251-254.

Jaynes, R. A. 1965. Nurse seed grafts of chestnut species and hybrids. Proc. Amer. Soc. Hort. Sci. 86:178-182.

Nelson, S. H. 1968. Incompatibility survey among horticultural plants. Proc. Inter. Plant Prop. Soc. 18:343-407.

Nicolin, P. 1953. Nicolieren, a new method of grafting. Proc. Inter. Plant Prop. Soc. 3:41-44.

Rogers, W. S. and A. B. Beakbone. 1957. Stock and scion relations. Ann. Rev. Plant Physiol. 8:217-236.

Ryan, G. F. 1970. Selection and time of collection of material for stocks and scions. Proc. Inter. Plant Prop. Soc. 20:225-231.

Sexton, D. 1966. Grafting of selected ornamentals. Proc. Inter. Plant Prop. Soc. 16:278-280.

Upshall, W. H. 1946. The stub graft as a supplement to budding in nursery practice. Proc. Amer. Soc. Hort. Sci. 47:187-189.

White, D. B. and J. P. Mahlstede. 1960. Compatibility in grafting and budding fruit and ornamental plants for adaption and dwarfing purposes. Proc. Inter. Plant Prop. Soc. 10:50-57.

Wildung, D. and H. Pellett. 1969. Relationship of rootstock in the apple to maturity and cold hardiness of the scion variety. Proc. Inter. Plant Prop. Soc. 19:364-371.

NOTES

LABORATORY PROJECT XIX. WHIP AND TONGUE GRAFTING.

PURPOSE:
To demonstrate the technique of Whip and Tongue grafting.

MATERIALS:
Scion wood: Apple (Malus sp.), willow (Salix sp.) branches or other
    suitable dormant material
Stock plants: Apple seedlings, willow branches or other suitable dormant
    material
Propagation knife
Labels
Pencil
Budding rubbers
Grafting wax
Grafting lamp
Paint brush
Potting medium
Pots
(Optional: nurserymen's tape)

PROCEDURE:
1. Print a label for each plant to be grafted.
2. Prepare the stock.
   A. Make a smooth, oblique cut about 2.5 cm (1 in) long in the
      internode region.
   B. Make a second cut starting about one-third of the distance from
      the tip. It should be smooth and almost parallel to the first
      cut.
3. Prepare the scion by using the same procedures as for the stock.
4. Insert the scion into the stock so that the tongues interlock. The
   cambial layers on both sides should be matched closely. If the scion
   is smaller than the stock, match up the cambial layers on at least
   one side.
5. Wrap the graft securely with a budding rubber.
6. Wax the entire graft area with grafting wax.
7. Optional: wrap the graft with nurserymen's tape instead of a budding
   rubber. By overlapping the edges of the tape, waxing will not be
   necessary.
8. Pot the grafted plant and water.
9. Stick the label in one side of the pot.
10. Place the plant on the greenhouse bench.

RESULTS:
1. After 4-6 weeks remove the budding rubber. The graft union should be
   complete.

THOUGHT PROVOKERS

1. Is it essential that the scion wood be cut just previous to the time of grafting? Discuss the methods of handling scion wood.

2. What is the function of the wax or tape in a successful graft?

3. What is meant by double-working of fruit or ornamental trees? What are the advantages of this process?

LABORATORY PROJECT XX. CLEFT GRAFTING.

Before becoming a skilled or even a proficient grafter, you must learn and practice the techniques involved. While the cleft graft is most often used to topwork fruit trees, some herbaceous plants may also be cleft grafted, i.e., Hedera helix can be grafted onto Fatshedera lizei to obtain a special form - tree ivy.

PURPOSE:
To demonstrate the technique of cleft grafting, and to illustrate the physiological principles involved in the graft healing process.

MATERIALS:
Scion wood: Hedera helix
Stock plants: Fatshedera lizei
Propagation knife
Labels
Pencil
Polyethylene bags
Twist ties
Budding rubbers

PROCEDURE:
1. Collect two terminal shoots of scion wood 15 cm (6 in) in length for each graft.
2. Remove the top of the stock plant by making a smooth cut at a right angle to the stem axis. (This top portion may be used as a cutting to start new stock plants for the future.)
3. Make a split down the center of the stem about 2.5 cm (1 in) long.
4. Prepare the scions by making a long, tapering cut 2.5 cm (1 in) long down one side and then the other.
5. Insert the scions into each end of the split in the stock. Try to match the cambial layers as closely as possible.
6. Wrap the graft with a budding rubber. It should be just tight enough to hold the scions in place.
7. Cover the plant with a polyethylene bag and tie it below the graft union with a twist tie. It should be secure but not too tight.
8. Prepare and place a label in each pot for proper identification.
9. Place the grafted plant under the greenhouse bench out of direct sunlight or under intermittent mist.

RESULTS:
1. Examine the plants every few days to detect any irregularities such as wilting of the scion pieces.
2. After 4-5 weeks remove the twist ties.
3. Allow the polyethylene bag to remain on the plant for a week before removing it.

NOTES

THOUGHT PROVOKERS

1. What percentage of "takes" would you expect to obtain from a cleft graft-
    ing operation in a deciduous orchard in December? When is the best or
    optimum time for cleft grafting and what should be the condition of the
    stock and scion?

2. What effect will extreme temperatures (both high and low) during the
    healing process have on the cleft grafting process?

Budding

Literally dozens of methods or variations for budding have been described in the literature dealing with the propagation of plants. Budding methods have generally been divided into 2 categories, those in which the broad face of the cambial tissue is exposed on the stock (i.e., the T-bud or patch bud) and others in which the cambial layers must be aligned (i.e., the chip bud). Budding has also been described as bud grafting, in that it is a form of grafting where the scion has only a single bud.

T OR SHIELD BUDDING

T or shield budding is the most commonly used method for propagation of woody perennials because of its simplicity and efficiency. This operation is usually performed in the summer months, July and August, while the stock and scion are actively growing. One of the other major advantages of T-budding is that it can be used both for topworking young trees as well as in propagating desired individuals on seedlings or clonal rootstocks. Buds are normally inserted in shoots of the current season's growth, however, budding into 1 or 2 year old wood, as in the case of topworking, can be quite successful.

To perform a T bud, begin by selecting a straight section in the understock which is free from any lesions and between the nodes, and make a T cut through the bark (Figure 28 E & F). The vertical cut is generally made to a length of approximately 2.5 cm (1 in), with the horizontal cut about 1/2 this length. After making the T cut through the bark of the stock, use the backside of the knife to gently spread the bark from the wood. The bark must slip easily in order for this to be done properly (Figure 28 G). This T shaped cut is normally made at the base of seedling rootstocks at a point 5 to 25 cm (2-10 in) from the ground.

The bud is removed from the budstick by beginning to cut at about 1 cm (0.5 in) below the bud with a sharp knife. Cut into the wood slightly, then upward beneath the bud, coming out about 1 cm (0.5 in) above the bud. During this process the knife is allowed to penetrate the wood under the bud slightly, which leaves a small portion or sliver of wood under the bud on removal (Figure 28 A-D). Some professionals remove this sliver to attain greater cambial contact.

We need mention here that when cutting the budsticks for the day's budding operation, that as they are removed from the tree, the leaf blades should be clipped off, leaving a short piece of the petiole attached to the shoot (Figure 28 A & B). By leaving this petiole attached, the buds are easier to handle during the T budding operation, when they are cut off the budstick and ready to be placed into the stock.

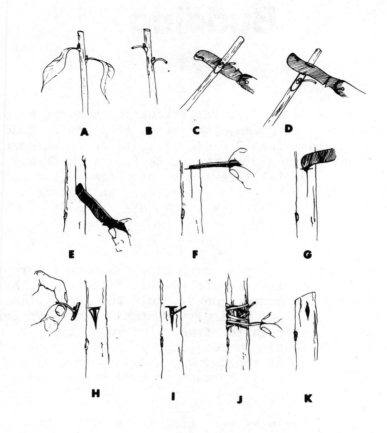

FIGURE 28.   T OR SHIELD BUDDING.

The next step in the budding operation is to insert the bud into the stock. This is done by grasping the petiole stub and gently pushing the shield shaped bud downward beneath the bark of the T-shaped cut in the stock (Figure 28 H & I). If the bark of the shield extends above the upper cross cut, then cut it off evenly, so that the under surface of the shield fits snugly to the wood of the stock. Perhaps the most important step of this budding operation is the wrapping of the inserted bud. To wrap with a budding rubber strip, start below the bud, cross the strip with the first turn to hold it in place, and continue to wrap up to the bud, then across the bud, but not over it, until all the cut surfaces are covered (Figure 28 J). In this way, the wrap is smoooth, and no knots are needed. Three or four wraps both above and below the cut are usually sufficient.

It is important to stress proper wrapping procedures as these will be the only protection the bud will have against drying out which often occurs on field-budded plants. If improperly wrapped, water can get in around the bud union, causing decay, while under similar conditions if the bud is exposed to air prior to healing, the developing cambial cells in the area of the bud union will dessicate.

The bud will usually remain dormant over the winter period. In the early spring when growth begins, the stock should be pruned off 1 to 2 cm (0.5-0.75 in) above the inserted bud. In the case of apples and pears, the stock may be cut off before growth begins, however with the stone fruits, it is best to delay the cutting until the new growth begins.

PATCH BUDDING

The patch budding method is generally used for thick barked trees, such as walnut and rubber trees. This differs from shield or T-budding in that the bark for <u>both</u> the stock and budsticks must be slipping or actively growing. To perform patch budding, special patch budding tools which consist of 2 pairs of blades, positioned to form a rectangle are required. Using scion wood and stock stems of similar diameters, the patch budder is placed in position on the understock, generally between nodes on a lesion-free, knot-free limb (Figure 29 D-E). The patch is removed and the operation is repeated on the scion budstick (Figure 29 A-C) to obtain the desired bud. This bud is then positioned in the vacated area on the understock (Figure 29 F-H).

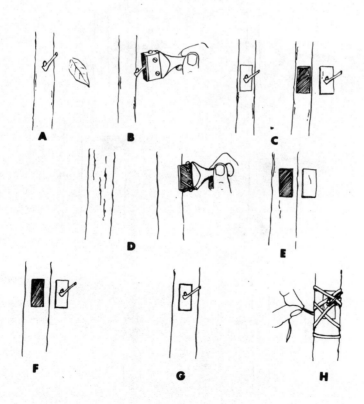

FIGURE 29. PATCH BUDDING.

After the bud is in place, it is secured with rubber budding strips or waxed string. If the patch is well fitting and has not buckled during the budding operation, or if the plants are to be placed under particularly humid conditions, there is no need to seal the union with grafting wax. However, if there is danger that the bud may dry out, the union should then be covered with grafting wax. The budding rubber strip or waxed string should be removed after callusing, to prevent girdling.

CHIP BUDDING

Chip budding is employed when the bark of either or both the stock or scion budstick is dormant and not slipping. Although environmental conditions may vary with geographical location, chip budding is commonly performed in the spring months, just prior to the first growth flush.

Select healthy scion budsticks and remove a terminal portion to eliminate the danger of using either immature buds or ones which have been winter injured. The buds are removed by placing the knife 1 to 2.5 cm (0.5-1 in) above the bud and making a sloping cut that extends just inside the wood to a point 0.6 to 1.3 cm (0.25-0.5 in) below the base of the bud (Figure 30 A & B). The knife is then placed in a position immediately below the bud, on the

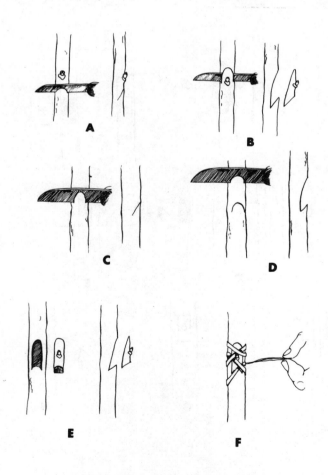

FIGURE 30. CHIP BUDDING.

outer surface of the bark and a sloping cut is made to contact the lower portion of the first incision.

The same procedure is repeated on the understock (Figure 30 C & D), the chip being removed and discarded. The desired scion bud is fitted into place, matching as much of the 2 cambium layers as is possible. After positioning, the bud should be tied securely with rubber grafting tape, rubber budding strips, or polyethylene strips (Figure 30 E & F).

SELECTED REFERENCE MATERIALS

Garner, R. J. 1968. The Grafters Handbook, 3rd Edition. Faber and Faber, Ltd., London.

Stang, E. J., D. C. Ferree and F. O. Hartman. 1978. Fruit tree propagation. Ohio Coop. Ext. Service Bull. 481.

NOTES

184

LABORATORY PROJECT XXI.   T OR SHIELD BUDDING.

PURPOSE:
To demonstrate the technique of T or shield budding.

MATERIALS:
Scion wood: Apple (Malus sp.) or other suitable deciduous material
Stock plants: Apple seedlings or other suitable deciduous material
Propagation knife
Labels
Pencil
Budding rubber strips
Potting medium
Pots

PROCEDURE:
1. Print a label for each plant to be budded.
2. Prepare the stock by making a T-shaped cut into the bark.
   A. Make a straight vertical cut about 2.5 cm (1 in) long.
   B. Make a second cut perpendicular to the top of the first about
      1 cm (0.5 in) long.
3. Using the tip of the knife, gently pull open the two flaps of bark.
4. Prepare the scion by removing a single bud from the budstick.
   A. Make a shallow slanted cut starting about 1 cm (0.5 in) on the
      stem below the bud and continuing about 1 cm (0.5 in) above
      the bud.
   B. Make a horizontal cut above the bud at the top of the first cut.
   C. Remove the "shield" of scion wood.
5. Insert the shield into the T-cut of the stock. The top of the shield
   should be level with the top of the T-cut. If it is not, recut the
   top of the shield.
6. Wrap the graft securely with a budding rubber by taking several turns
   above and below the bud. Do not cover the bud.
7. Pot the budded plant and water.
8. Stick the label in one side of the pot.
9. Place the plant on the greenhouse bench.

RESULTS:
1. After 3-5 weeks remove the budding rubber. The graft union should
   be complete.
2. Early the next spring, remove the stock above the bud.

THOUGHT PROVOKERS

1. Contrast the "wood-out" and "wood-in" methods of preparing the scion.

2. Draw the scion piece for inverted T-budding.

3. When should inverted T-budding be used instead of T-budding?

4. What causes the bark to "slip"? Why is this important in grafting?

LABORATORY PROJECT XXII. CHIP BUDDING.

PURPOSE:
>   To demonstrate the technique of chip budding.

MATERIALS:
>   Scion wood: Apple (Malus sp.) or other suitable deciduous material
>   Stock plants: Apple seedlings or other suitable material
>   Propagation knife
>   Label
>   Pencil
>   Budding rubber strips, nurserymen's tape or polyethylene strips
>   Potting medium
>   Pots

PROCEDURE:
1. Gather 2 pieces of suitable wood approximately 1.2 to 2.5 cm (0.5-1 in) in diameter.
2. Begin by making a cut 1/4 the way through the stock at a 45° angle.
3. Make a second cut, starting about 2.5 cm (1 in) above the first, going inward and downward until it connects with the first cut.
4. Select a healthy bud on the budstick and begin by making a cut 0.5 cm (0.25 in) below the bud at a 45° angle. Make this cut approximately 1/4 the distance through the budstick.
5. Make a second cut, beginning 1.2 cm (0.5 in) above the bud and proceed inward and downward toward the first cut. Remove the bud piece.
6. Carefully insert the chip bud into the stock and wrap with nurserymen's adhesive tape, budding rubber strips or polyethylene strips.

RESULTS:
1. After 3-5 weeks remove the protective rubber strip or nurserymen's adhesive tape.
2. Examine the graft union for healing.

NOTES

190

THOUGHT PROVOKERS

1. Discuss the advantages and disadvantages of chip budding.

2. Why might chip budding be useful in the spring, as compared to "T" or patch budding?

Layering

L. H. Bailey writing in "The Nursery Manual" published in 1898 defined a layer as a "shoot or root attached to the parent plant, partially or wholly covered with earth, with the intention that it take root and then be severed from the parent".

Thus layering or layerage is the process of forming roots on a stem while it is still attached to the plant. This is in contrast to inducing root formation on a detached stem (cutting). In addition, it should be noted that layering is a natural phenomenon with some types of plants and it does serve as a natural means of propagation.

Layering is still widely practiced in some commercial nurseries in Holland and England, but it has never been particularly popular in the United States for one main reason; it is a slow process and requires some skilled attention. When propagating some plants that will not root easily from cuttings or where grafting is not practical one can resort to layering. Many plants can be propagated in limited numbers by air layerage. Layerage does not require the skilled techniques of grafting or the close attention to the environmental conditions necessary for rooting cuttings. It is an ideal method for the home gardener to renew an old plant or to produce a limited number of new plants from an existing one. A layer (the stem on which roots are formed) is supported by the parent plant from which it draws water and nutrients during root development.

The first requirement for many types of layering is a properly grown, healthy, well-established mother plant. By properly grown we mean the plant was selected several growing seasons prior to being used as a mother plant and the shoots have been pinched to develop a well-branched system of stems. The second requirement of great importance is a well-drained sandy loam soil to be used for the layering bed. In order for layering to occur the soil must be in a condition similar to that of the soil found in the greenhouse bench used for rooting of cuttings. It is generally necessary for a period of time prior to the layering operation that the nurseryman or homeowner should cultivate the layering bed and add sand, peat, composted sawdust or other material that will make it loose and friable.

COMMON OR SIMPLE LAYERING

This method of layering can be done with many deciduous or evergreen plants. With deciduous plants simple layering is usually done in the spring using long low branches that are produced during the previous growth season, although layering done with current season shoots can also be performed. One year old branches can also be used for broadleaf evergreens, such as magnolia or rhododendron. (<u>Tip layering</u>, as commonly practiced or occurring naturally in blackberry or black raspberry, involves the branch tip merely touching the soil and rooting at that point.)

To layer a deciduous or broadleaf evergreen plant, bend a branch to the ground into a hole or trench about 15 cm (6 in) deep, bend the branch up sharply about 30 cm (12 in) from the tip and cover the bent portion with soil while leaving about 15 cm (6 in) of the tip exposed (Figure 31 A). Remove the leaves that will be covered with soil. In some cases a wire loop or wooden peg is needed over the lowest point of the bend to hold the branch in the soil. It may be necessary to stake the protruding shoot tip to hold it upright (Figure 31 B).

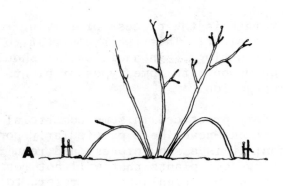

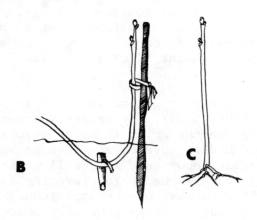

FIGURE 31.   COMMON OR SIMPLE LAYERING.

Rooting of the layer can be stimulated by a shallow cut or notch in the underside of the shoot at the point of the bend. This also makes bending easier on very stiff stems. In addition, a root promoting compound may be applied to the cut in order to induce root formation. After the layering operation is completed, proper watering and weed control are major concerns.

If deciduous plants are layered in August or September it is desirable to place a mulch on the surface of the ground in and around the mother plant to protect it from cold damage during the subsequent winter. The mulch is removed in the spring. In addition, if mulch is used, field mice, moles and other rodents may girdle the stem during severe winters so nurserymen may often place poison baits or repellants around the mother plant.

Branches that are layered in the spring should be well rooted by fall and can be severed from the parent plant after they have become dormant (Figure 31 C). These rooted layers can be transplanted either that fall or the following spring before growth begins. It is a common practice not to dig those layered individuals during the summer, but to wait until the following spring. If the top of the new layer is large in proportion to the root system, it is advisable to prune the top to reduce the size so that water demands for the top can be met by the root system.

COMPOUND OR SERPENTINE LAYERING
Compound layering is commonly used on plants with long flexible vine type stems such as grape, wisteria or clematis. The theory behind compound layering is similar to that of simple layering only there is more of it. The branch is laid on the ground and soil is used to cover the area between the buds. When compound layering, one should make sure that each exposed portion of the stem has one or more leaves attached as this assures that a bud will be present to form a shoot for each new plant. The stem should root at each location and after rooting, the stem is cut into sections such that each portion contains roots, a node and a shoot bud. The time of layering, digging, and method of handling are the same as that for simple layers (Figure 32).

MOUND OR STOOL LAYERING
Plants of some species such as Malus rootstocks and Cydonia and Ribes, which have stiff branches that do not bend easily to the soil, can often be propagated by mound layering. In addition, if a well established shrub can be sacrificed for a period of one year, many new plants can be produced from it by mound layering.

Basically, mound layering involves cutting back the parent plant so that the new shoots develop at the base (Figure 33). Prior to the initiation of the new spring growth the parent plant is cut back to about 5 to 8 cm (2-3 in) of the ground (Figure 33 C). Several shoots will usually develop from the crown (Figure 33 D). Once the new shoots are 8-10 cm (3-4 in) long, soil is mounded around the plant so that the bases of the new shoots are covered to about 1/2 their length with soil (Figure 33 E-F). Add soil 2 or 3 times throughout the growing season as the shoot continues to grow. Final depth of the soil surrounding these new shoots should be about 20 to 25 cm (8-10 in) or about 1/2 their height. Usually at the end of the growing season roots have obtained enough growth whereby the rooted shoots can be removed very close to the base of the plant and lined out in the nursery row (Figure 33 G). If shoots are removed in the fall it is a common practice to re-cover the original plant with soil until spring to protect it from winter damage. More plants can be produced each year for several years after the mounding process has started.

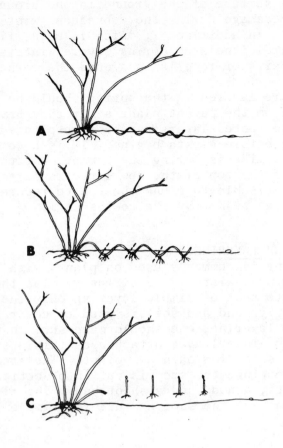

FIGURE 32.   COMPOUND OR SERPENTINE LAYERING.

    If established plants are not available to mound layer, a new plant can
be planted and allowed to grow for one year and then handled as previously
described. Even if the plant has only one stem it will generally produce 6
or more shoots which can be layered.

    Soil conditions in the area where this type of layering is to be per-
formed should be porous and well drained. Sawdust and composted wood shavings
are sometimes used for mounding instead of soil. The mound should be kept
moist at all times, since drying will slow the rooting process or destroy
roots already formed.

TRENCH OR CONTINUOUS LAYERING
    Trench or continuous layering is an alternate method to mound layering
that is often used by nurserymen to propagate rootstocks for fruit and nut
trees. Like other methods of layering, trench layering implies that we obtain layers for new plants from a trench. The mother plant is transplanted
in the row at an angle 30 to 45° and allowed to grow for a period of one

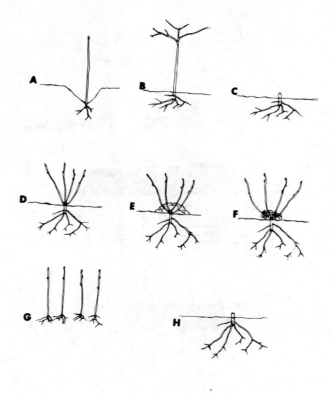

FIGURE 33.   MOUND OR STOOL LAYERING.

year (Figure 34 A).   The following spring before growth begins a 5 to 8 cm
(2-3 in) trench is opened in the direction the plant is leaning (Figure 34 B).
Then the plant is placed in the bottom of the trench and held flatly against
the soil with wire loops or wooden pegs (Figure 34 C).   Remove weak thin
branches or cut them back severely at this time.   Prior to the initiation of
bud development in the spring cover the plant with about 2 to 3 cm (1-1.5 in)
of soil, composted sawdust or wood shavings.   New shoots from buds on the
plants will develop through the 2.5 cm (1 in) covering of soil (Figure 34 D-
E).   Add more soil as the shoots elongate.   The process from this point is
much like that described for mound layering.   At the end of the growing season
roots should have developed adequately to remove the soil and cut away the
root layers (Figure 34 F).   The mother plant remains in the trench as there
will probably be other shoots partially grown that have not developed an
adequate root system.

A similar method called continuous layerage is often used on ornamental
shrubs or other plants with long stems which can be bent to the ground.   In
this case the long stem is placed in the trench and covered over entirely
except for the tip which is left exposed.   New shoots will develop from the

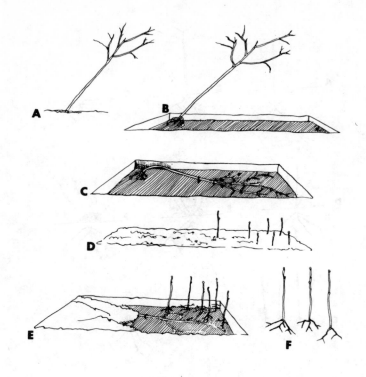

FIGURE 34.   TRENCH LAYERING.

buds along the stem. They should usually be mounded as described above to develop a greater area for root formation at the stem base.

AIR LAYERING

   Air layering is a method of obtaining a few offspring of woody or semi-woody shrubs. This method of propagation is used to some extent commercially for propagating some species such as Ficus elastica (Rubber Plant) yet it is simple enough to be successfully employed by amateur gardeners. The method is simple because conditions are provided for roots to form, while the part which becomes the "new plant" is still attached to the stock plant.

   Air layering is a specific type of layering. Besides being a method of propagation, air layering can be used to "shorten" overly tall or spindly plants which have become unattractive because of the loss of lower leaves. All that is required for air layering is sphagnum moss, peat or similar material, a water-proof wrapping material (polyethylene), electrician's tape, string or twist-ties and a stock plant.

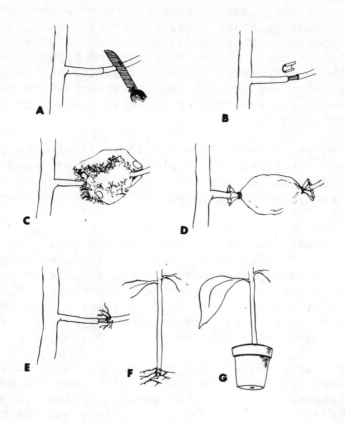

FIGURE 35.   AIR LAYERING.

Selection of shoots to be air layered is important. It is practically useless to propagate plants which are diseased or have been damaged by insects. Choose a branch about pencil thickness (or larger) where there is a section about 15 cm (6 in) in length (cut off some leaves if necessary). Using a sturdy, sharp propagation knife make 2 girdling cuts down to hardwood, about 2 cm (0.75 in) apart (Figure 25 A & B). Scrape off all the <u>bark and green cambium layer</u>, between the 2 girdling cuts. Complete or partial girdling by removing the bark or wounding will usually induce quicker rooting of woody plants. The downward movement of carbohydrates is stopped at the girdle, thus encouraging root formation. Water can still move upward into the shoot to keep the leaves turgid. After complete or partial girdling, one of the commercial rooting powders can be lightly dusted on the cut area. It is not necessary to use rooting substances, but earlier rooting often results if they are used. Alternative methods of achieving similar results include various types of cuts partially through the stem which are propped open in some manner.

Moist sphagnum moss is best to use for air layering because it is fibrous with good aeration, is fungistatic, easy to apply to the stem and holds in place while tying. Peat or other similar material can be used, although sphagnum moss is superior. Whatever is used, excessive water should be squeezed out with the fingers before wrapping and tying. One "handful" of moss placed over the girdled area is usually sufficient (Figure 35 C). One of the best materials to use to wrap the sphagnum moss is polyethylene (Figure 35 D). Water does not penetrate polyethylene although it allows diffusion of oxygen and carbon dioxide.

After wrapping, the polyethylene should be firmly secured above and below the mossed area with either electrician's tape or twist-ties. A fairly tight seal is necessary to prevent evaporation of water as well as leakage of water into the sphagnum during rains. If excess water accumulates, rooting will not take place.

Because of the water content of the sphagnum moss, the air layer should be completed and removed prior to the arrival of winter if done on outdoor plants. By using the transparent polyethylene plastic wrapping, roots can be seen developing in the sphagnum moss in a few weeks. When the sphagnum moss is well-filled with roots, it should be removed from the parent plant. Remove the new plant and carefully remove the polyethylene wrapping surrounding the roots and proceed with potting (Figure 35 E-G).

The length of time required for roots to form will vary with the plant. Roses often form roots in four weeks, while viburnums and magnolias often require most of the growing season. In general, outdoor woody plants should be layered in early spring so that roots will form and the new plants can be separated and planted before winter.

SELECTED REFERENCE MATERIALS

Chase, H. H. 1965. Propagation of oriental magnolias by layering. Proc. Inter. Plant Prop. Soc. 15:334-337.

Ching, F., C. L. Hammer and F. Widmoyer. 1956. Air-layering with polyethylene film. Mich. Agri. Exp. Sta. Quart. Bull. 39:3-9.

Feucht, J. R., D. D. Watson and F. L. S. O'Rourke. 1961. Air-layering of Picea glauca and Pinus sylvestris. Proc. Amer. Soc. Hort. Sci. 77:578-582.

Larsen, F. E. 1976. Layering to renew or multiply plants. Pacific Northwest Cooperative Ext. Pub. 165.

Wagner, G. 1965. Propagating apple rootstocks by the method of continuous layering. Proc. Inter. Plant Prop. Soc. 15:334-337.

LABORATORY PROJECT XXIII. AIR LAYERING.

PURPOSE:
To demonstrate the technique of air layerage.

MATERIALS:
Ficus elastica, Brassaia actinophylla, Dieffenbachia sp., Dracaena sp., Fatshedera lizei or other suitable material
Propagation knife
Labels
Pencil
Polyethylene sheets, 20-25 cm on a side or polyethylene bags
Twist-ties
Sphagnum moss (moistened - not wet)
Potting medium and pots

PROCEDURE:
1. Print a label for each plant to be air layered.
2. Girdle the stem 15 to 30 cm (6-12 in) from the tip.
3. Make another girdle 2 to 4 cm (1-1.5 in) below the first.
4. Join the two girdling cuts with a vertical cut.
5. Remove the strip of bark and carefully scrape the exposed tissue.
6. Place a handful of moistened sphagnum moss firmly around the wounded area.
7. Completely enclose the sphagnum moss with a square of polyethylene. Fold the ends of the square together to form a cylinder.
8. Secure the top and bottom of the polyethylene with twist-ties.
9. Stick the label in one side of the pot.
10. Place the layered plant on a bench out of direct sunlight.

RESULTS:
1. Examine the layer weekly to observe the progress of root formation.
2. After 8 weeks, roots should be clearly visible through the polyethylene.
3. Remove the layer (new plant) from the parent plant below the rooted area and trim off the stub.
4. Pot the layer in the medium and water.
5. Enclose the layer in a large polyethylene bag. (Curved coat hangers may be used as a frame.)
6. Secure the bag around the sides of the pot.
7. Allow the polyethylene bag to remain on the plant for a week before removing it.

NOTES

202

THOUGHT PROVOKERS

1. What are the advantages of roots developing on a stem while still attached to the parent plant?

2. What influence might the carbohydrate-nitrogen relationship have on successful propagation of plants by layers?

3. What types of layering are practiced today on a commercial basis? Why can many plants be reproduced by these methods, when they fail to propagate from cuttings?

4. When air layering is performed outdoors, foil is usually wrapped around the polyethylene as a second covering. Why?

5. After the layer is removed from the parent plant, is the parent plant of any value? Explain.

6. Why might a slanting cut be used for air layering instead of the girdling method?

Seed Propagation

Seed propagation is a practice followed in the production of many hardy trees and shrubs. In fact, it is the usual method of propagation for a number of both wild and cultivated species. A large number of woody plants can be satisfactorily reproduced from seed with little variation in the character of the seedling. However, for fruit and many other ornamental crops, where the expressed purpose of propagation is to reproduce a clone, some other means of propagation, i.e., layering, grafting or cuttings, is required.

Seeds of horticultural crops may be classified as those that require special treatment such as scarification or stratification and those that germinate quickly upon sowing, even after an extended period of dry storage. The class of seeds that requires special handling conditions are generally characterized by the fact that the fruits or seed-bearing parts should be ripe when they are harvested. The seed itself is not capable of germination upon harvest and in order to secure successful germination, it becomes necessary to overcome factors such as dormancy, rest or inhibiting seed coats.

Seeds of many plant species do not germinate readily for various reasons or combinations of reasons and it is necessary to understand several terms.

Seed dormancy is an all inclusive term indicating that seed will not germinate and produce seedlings due to unfavorable environmental or internal conditions (the inhibitory factors may be external, internal or a combination of both).

Quiescence relates to the fact that seed will not germinate and produce seedlings due to unfavorable external conditions. Contributing factors are moisture, temperature, oxygen, light, or others such as pH, nutrients, carbon dioxide, or toxic conditions. This can be overcome by simply supplying the absent factor or factors in optimum amounts during germination.

Rest or internal dormancy describes the situation where seed will not germinate due to unfavorable factors or conditions specific to the seed. These may be classified in the following eight areas: seed coat, endosperm, embryo development, embryo rest, epicotyl rest, root and epicotyl rest, cotyledons, and combinations of these. The inhibitory action of these factors or conditions can be overcome by seed coat treatments, furnishing food materials, cold temperatures, warm temperatures, combinations of warm and cold temperatures, the use of light, leaching, and possibly chemical treatments.

After-ripening is basically a series of physiological or chemical changes occurring within the seed which bring to a close the rest period and makes germination possible. Conditions favoring after-ripening include cold temperature, warm temperature, alternating temperatures, ample oxygen, moist stratification and probably light.

Important changes which have been found to occur in some seeds during after-ripening are increases in water-holding capacity, acidity, enzyme activity (specifically catalase, peroxidase, and oxidase), sugar content, amino acid content, stored protein, respiration, and vigor of the seed which is believed to reduce susceptibility to fungal incidence.

CHARACTERISTICS OF GOOD SEED
It is often impossible to conduct a quick, preliminary laboratory test on the soundness of seeds. Good seed may often be judged by the following criteria:
1. It should be gathered so as to be sufficiently mature.
2. It should be gathered from a group of individuals rather than from isolated plants. (This does not apply to self-pollinated individuals.)
3. The seed should be plump and firm and when placed in water, good seed sinks, while poor or nonviable seed floats.
4. The seed should be fresh and preferably not more than 1 year old; or if so, it should have been properly stored.
5. The seed should not have been heated or fermented so as to have a detrimental effect and it should be free of insect, disease or rodent injury.

SEED TREATMENT
In a natural situation seeds fall to the ground and some quickly become covered with leaves and soil. The natural winter rains keep the seeds moist and along with the cold temperatures the dormancy conditions of many native tree and shrub seeds are satisfied.

While this process occurs naturally, nurserymen accomplish the same task through the process of "stratification". Stated simply, stratification is the pretreatment of seeds by storing them in a moist substance at carefully controlled temperatures to condition them for rapid germination upon completion of a specified time period. In general, the medium used for stratification is a 50:50 mixture of moist peat and sand. This medium should not contain free or standing water because this interferes with the entrance of air and creates conditions favorable for rotting or other decay organisms. To avoid this possibility, the bottom of the container is often perforated so that any excess water can be drained way.

In practice, a layer of the medium from 2.5-7.5 cm (1-3 in) in depth is place at the bottom of the container, followed by a similar layer of seed. The process is repeated until the container is filled. Small lots of seed, or seed difficult to separate from the medium at planting time are often enclosed in cheesecloth sacks and flattened out to form layers. Wire screening, hardware cloth or perforated plastic bags folded to form a flat package are also satisfactory. These materials have the additional merit of not rotting, as cheesecloth often does, during stratification periods of long duration.

Sometimes, especially for larger seeds from numerous tree species, e.g., oak, hickory, and walnut, the seeds are simply mixed with 2 or 3 times their volume of the medium and placed in containers, observing the same precautions as to moisture and drainage as that in traditional stratification. When using this method, or whenever the seed must be separated from the medium at planting time, screening with a diameter smaller than that of the seed allows for an easy and convenient method of seed recovery.

Storage places for seed during the stratification period may include a refrigerator, cold storage box, root cellar or any place where temperatures can be maintained between 2 and 7°C (35-45°F).

While many seeds can be removed and immediately stratified with no pre-liminary handling, there are those individuals which require that the seed coat be damaged in some manner so that oxygen and/or moisture can reach the embryo. These pretreatments, which can include a hot water soak, acid or mechanical scarification, are quite often necessary for seeds which have thick, hard seed coats.

Treating seeds with hot water is accomplished by placing the seeds in bags of cheesecloth or a similar porous material and plunging them into water heated 82-93°C (180-200°F), in which they are allowed to stand for about 12 to 24 hours, as the water gradually cools. The volume of water should be 4 to 5 times that of the seed.

Acid scarification is generally the most satisfactory method of pre-treating seed prior to stratification. The seed is placed in a glass, earthenware, or nonmetallic container and covered with concentrated sulfuric acid for a predetermined period of time depending on species. During the treatment period the seed is gently stirred.

The seed is separated from the sulfuric acid by pouring into a wire mesh strainer, thereby retaining the seed. At this point the seed should be washed with copious amounts of water to remove all traces of the acid. The seed, after thorough washing, should be dried for easier handling, and at this point either sown or stratified.

Mechanical scarification is a very common method used to overcome seed coat dormancy by many seedsmen and nurserymen who handle large quantities of seed. The mechanical methods of scarifying seed are not as satisfactory as the sulfuric acid treatment for small seed lots or for infrequent usage, because considerable equipment is needed unless one is to avoid excessive manual labor.

For small lots of large-sized seed, scarification can sometimes be accomplished by using a hand file. This method is slow and costly and the danger of injury to the embryo is great. For larger quantities of both large and small sized seed, mechanical scarification is accomplished by such means as tumbling or turning the seeds in drums lined with sandpaper. Seeds may also be mixed with clean, sharp gravel and rotated or tumbled until the seed coats are sufficiently thin so as not to be a further hindrance to germination.

Other devices involve passing the seed between rotating sandpaper disks or grinding wheels.

None of these scarification methods are satisfactory for seeds containing resin or pulpy remains of fleshy seed coat as these materials quickly destroy the cutting action of the abrasive. In general, mechanical methods for scarifying seeds require greater skill and experience in order to obtain results as uniform as that from acid treatments.

Recommendations for the propagation via seeds of numerous woody species can be found in "seeds of woody plants of the United States" (see rererence list).

SELECTED REFERENCE MATERIALS

Barton, L. V. 1953. Seed storage and viability . Contr. Boyce Thompson Inst. 17:87-103.

Barton, L. V. 1954. Effect of subfreezing temperatures on viability of conifer seeds in storage. Contr. Boyce Thompson Inst. 18:21-24.

Bass, L. N., T. M. Ching and F. L. Winter. 1961. Packages that Protect Seeds. In Seeds, The Yearbook of Agriculture. U.S.D.A., Washington, D.C. pp. 330-335.

Bonner, F. T. 1974. Seed testing. In Seeds of Woody Plants in the United States. Agri. Handbook #450. Forest Service, U.S. Dept. Agri., Washington, D.C. pp. 136-152.

Heit, C. E. 1950. Germination of sensitive flower seed kinds and varieties with suggested methods for testing in the laboratory. Proc. Assoc. Off. Seed Anal. 40:107-117.

Heit, C. E. 1955. The excised embryo method for testing germination quality of dormant seed. Proc. Assoc. Off. Seed Anal. 45:108-117.

Heit, C. E. 1964. The importance of quality, germinative characteristics and source for successful seed germination and plant production. Proc. Inter. Plant Prop. Soc. 14:74-85.

Parker, J. 1953. New methods for the determination of forest seed germinability. J. Forestry 51:34.

Schopmeyer, C. S. (Editor). 1974. Seeds of woody plants of the United States. U.S. Dept. Agri. For. Service. Agri. Handbook No. 450. Washington, D.C.

Toole, E. H. 1955. Interaction of temperature and light in the germination of seeds. Plant Physiol. 30:473-478.

LABORATORY PROJECT XXIV.   PRECONDITIONING WOODY PLANT SEEDS.

     The seed has three basic parts: (1) the embryo, (2) the food storage
tissue, and (3) the seed coat. The embryo and/or seed coat of woody seeds may
require special preconditioning in order to overcome dormancy before germination will occur.

     Some seeds require a period of low temperatures for physiological changes
or after-ripening to take place within the embryo before germination. The
process of stratification will meet this requirement. The seed coat which
protects the embryo from injury may be hard and impermeable to water. This
will prevent the seed from imbibing the water necessary for germination to
begin. In order to modify or alter this condition of the seed coat, the
seeds should be scarified. Scarification can be accomplished by several
methods - mechanical scarification, soaking the seeds in water, or acid
treatment. For seeds which require special preconditioning for both the
embryo and the seed coat (double dormancy), a combination of stratification
and scarification may be necessary.

     Although these special dormancy requirements are met in nature, germina-
tion may occur at irregular intervals. Not only is more time required, but
the resulting plants will be different ages and sizes. To the plant propagator, the uniformity of plant material is essential to his production cycle.
By using special preconditioning techniques it is possible to control the
germination of woody seeds.

PURPOSE:
     To demonstrate several preconditioning methods used to stimulate the
germination of woody plant seeds and explain the concepts of seed dormancy,
stratification, and scarification.

PART I: SCARIFICATION

<u>MATERIALS</u>:

<u>Robinia</u> <u>pseudoacacia</u>, <u>Gleditsia</u> <u>triacanthos</u>, <u>Gymnocladus</u> <u>dioicus</u>
Labels
Pencil
Beakers
Concentrated H_2SO_4 (sulfuric acid)
Mesh screens
Propagation medium in flats

<u>PROCEDURE</u>:
1. Print a label for each treatment.
   <u>Treatments</u>
   1. Control
   2. Hot water soak (seeds placed in $90^{o}C$ water and allowed to cool overnight).
   3. 30 min H_2SO_4
   4. 60 min H_2SO_4
2. Count out lots of 25 seeds for each treatment.
3. Acid soak - <u>BE CAREFUL</u>!! You are using <u>concentrated</u> <u>acid</u>. Do not get any on your skin or clothing. If any comes in contact with your skin, wash it off immediately with water.
   a. Place one lot of seeds into each of two beakers.
   b. Immerse the seeds in concentrated H_2SO_4 (1 part seeds to 2 parts acid).
   c. Allow one lot of seed to soak for 30 min and the other for 60 min.
   d. After soaking the seeds, pour them into the mesh screens and wash them thoroughly with water.
4. Sow the seeds in the propagation flat.

<u>RESULTS</u>:
1. After 3 weeks record the results of your experiment in the data summary table.

DATA SUMMARY TABLE

Treatment	Number of Seeds Per Lot	Number of Seeds Germinated	% Germination
1. Control			
2. Hot water soak			
3. 30 min H_2SO_4			
4. 60 min H_2SO_4			

PART II: STRATIFICATION

MATERIALS:
Pinus strobus, Malus sp. or other suitable seed
Labels
Pencil
Propagation medium in flats

PROCEDURE:
1. Print a label for each treatment.
    ### Treatments
    1. Control
    2. 30 days at $4.5^{o}C$
    3. 60 days at $4.5^{o}C$
2. Count out lots of 25 seeds for each treatment.
3. Sow the seeds in the propagation flat.

RESULTS:
1. After 3 weeks following the sowing of the stratified seed record your
   results in the data summary table.

DATA SUMMARY TABLE

Treatment	Number of Seeds Per Lot	Number of Seeds Germinated	% Germination
1. Control			
2. 30 days at $4.5^{o}C$			
3. 60 days at $4.5^{o}C$			

PART III: COMBINATION SCARIFICATION-STRATIFICATION TREATMENTS

MATERIALS:

Cercis canadensis or other suitable seed
Labels
Pencil
Beakers
Acid - concentrated H_2SO_4
Mesh screens
Propagation medium in flats

PROCEDURE:

1. Print a label for each treatment.

   Treatments
   1. Control
   2. Hot water soak
   3. 30 min H_2SO_4
   4. 60 min H_2SO_4
   5. 30 days at $4.5^{o}C$
   6. 60 days at $4.5^{o}C$
   7. 30 min H_2SO_4 + 30 days at $4.5^{o}C$
   8. 30 min H_2SO_4 + 60 days at $4.5^{o}C$
   9. 60 min H_2SO_4 + 30 days at $4.5^{o}C$
   10. 60 min H_2SO_4 + 60 days at $4.5^{o}C$

2. Count out lots of 25 seeds for each treatment.
3. Acid soak - BE CAREFUL!! You are using concentrated acid. Do not get any on your skin or clothing. If any comes in contact with your skin, wash it off immediately with water.
   a. Place one lot of seeds into each of two beakers.
   b. Immerse the seeds in concentrated H_2SO_4 (1 part seeds to 2 parts acid).
   c. Allow one lot to soak for 30 min and the other for 60 min.
   d. After soaking the seeds, pour them into the mesh screens and wash them thoroughly with water.
4. Sow the seeds in the propagation flat.

RESULTS:

1. After 3 weeks following the sowing of the seed record your results in the data summary table.

DATA SUMMARY TABLE

Treatment	Number of Seeds Per Lot	Number of Seeds Germinated	% Germination
1. Control			
2. Hot water soak			
3. 30 min H_2SO_4			
4. 60 min H_2SO_4			
5. 30 days at $4.5^{o}C$			
6. 60 days at $4.5^{o}C$			
7. 30 min H_2SO_4 + 30 days at $4.5^{o}C$			
8. 30 min H_2SO_4 + 60 days at $4.5^{o}C$			
9. 60 min H_2SO_4 + 30 days at $4.5^{o}C$			
10. 60 min H_2SO_4 + 60 days at $4.5^{o}C$			

NOTES

DATA EVALUATION

1. From Part I, prepare a bar graph based on your results from this experiment. Plot the percent germination values below.

   A) Comparison of 3 scarification treatments on % germination.

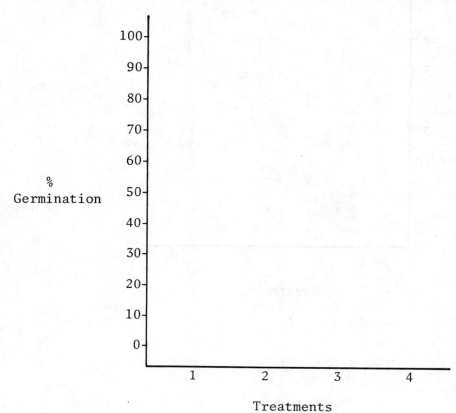

2. From Part II, prepare a bar graph based on your results from this experiment. Plot the mean % germination values for each treatment.

B) Comparison of 30 and 60 days of cold stratification on % germination.

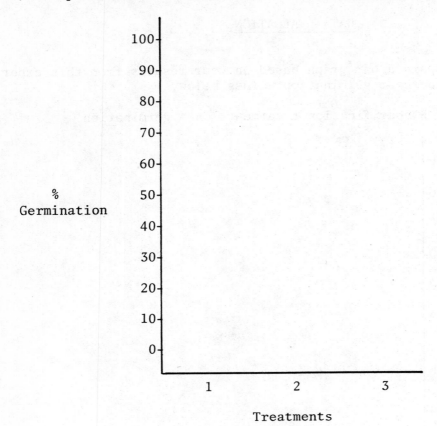

3. From Part III, prepare a bar graph based on your results from this experiment. Plot the mean % germination values for each treatment.

   A) A comparison of stratification and scarification treatments in various
      combinations on % germination.

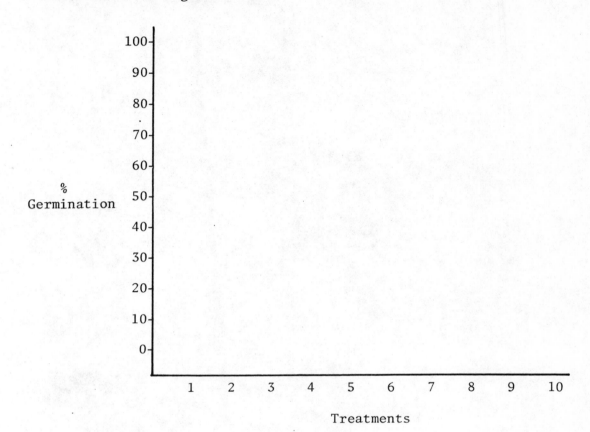

THOUGHT PROVOKERS

1. Describe 3 methods of <u>mechanical</u> scarification, and discuss under what conditions each might be used in a horticultural enterprise.

2. Besides modifying the hard seed coat, what other purposes may be accomplished by soaking the seeds in water?

3. How does scarification occur in nature?

4. How could too severe a scarification treatment affect the germination process?

Still another type of dormancy is noted in certain seeds which require exposure to light before they will germinate. In certain cultivars of lettuce, light in the red portion of the spectrum is required to break seed dormancy, however, this dormancy can quickly be re-imposed by a brief exposure of the seed to light in the far-red (fr) portion of the spectrum. Exposure of the imbibed seed to red light causes the phytochrome system to change to phytochrome fr, which is linked in some way to reactions inducing germination. Exposure of the seed to far-red light produces an instantaneous change to an alternate form, phytochrome r, which inhibits germination. In the dark and in the presence of oxygen at a low temperature, the latter change takes place slowly. In plants grown under natural light, the red wavelengths of the spectrum dominate, so that the phytochrome is converted to the active phytochrome fr form.

PURPOSE:
    To demonstrate the photo-reversible control of seed germination.

MATERIALS:
    'Grand Rapids' Lettuce (Lactuca sativa) or Peppergrass (Lepidium vir-
        ginicum) seed
    Petri dishes
    Filter paper
    Black sateen cloth bags made of 2 layers of cloth (large enough to
        hold each dish), light tight boxes or light tight black polyethylene
        bags with twist-ties
    Red and dark blue cellophane
    Distilled water

PROCEDURE:
    1. Presoak the lettuce or peppergrass overnight (about 16 hr).
    2. Prepare the 4 petri dishes by placing a sheet of filter paper in each
       and add 4 mls of distilled water to each.
    3. Place 25 imbibed seed in each dish.
    4. Immediately place the petri dishes, with lids on, in the light tight
       boxes or in the black cloth bags. Keep the temperature as close to
       21°C (70°F) as possible.
    5. In complete darkness, remove and label dishes A and B and expose to
       red light for 5 minutes.
    6. Return dish A to the darkness without further exposure to light.
    7. Expose dish B to 15 minutes of far-red light and place it immediately
       in the darkness.
    8. Place petri-dish D in room light.
    9. The 4 petri dishes with imbibed seed have now received their treat-
       ments. Dish C has remained in the dark and serves as a control. Dish
       A has been exposed to red radient energy for 5 minutes, dish B has
       been exposed to red light for 5 minutes and far-red for 15 minutes
       and dish D is a daylight control.

<u>RESULTS:</u>
1. Allow 3 or 4 days to elapse, then remove the dishes from the dark and record the number of germinated seeds.
2. Determine the percent germination.

DATA SUMMARY TABLE

Treatment	Number of Seeds Germinated	% Germination
Dish A (Red Light)		
Dish B (Red/Far Red Light)		
Dish C (Dark Control)		
Dish D (Light Control)		

DATA EVALUATION

1. Prepare a bar graph based on an evaluation of your results. Plot the percent germination for each treatment.

   A) The effect of red and far-red light on percent germination of 'Grand Rapids' lettuce seed.

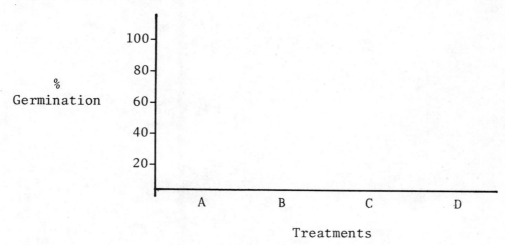

THOUGHT PROVOKERS

1. Based on your results, what do you believe is the nature of the photo-reversible control of germination?

2. What other processes are believed to be controlled by the phytochrome process? How are these other processes controlled?

LABORATORY PROJECT XXVI.   INFLUENCE OF VARIOUS CHEMICAL FACTORS ON SEED GERMINATION.

In the propagation of seeds, a number of products including gibberellic acid, thiourea, potassium nitrate and various cytokinins have been used to stimulate the germination of dormant seed. These products have also been noted in some cases to increase the rate of germination and stimulate seedling growth.

PURPOSE:

To demonstrate the effects of several growth regulators on seed germination.

MATERIALS:

'Grand Rapids' Lettuce (Lactuca sativa) or Kentucky Bluegrass (Poa pratensis)
Petri dishes
Distilled H_2O
1000 ppm gibberellic acid (GA)
5000 ppm thiourea
1000 ppm potassium nitrate (KNO_3)

PROCEDURE:

1. Place a piece of filter paper in the bottom of each petri dish.
2. Place 50 dry 'Grand Rapids' lettuce or Kentucky Bluegrass seeds in each dish.
3. Add 5 mls of distilled water to petri dish A.
4. Add 5 mls of a 1000 ppm solution of gibberellic acid to petri dish B.
5. Add 5 mls of a 5000 ppm solution of thiourea to petri dish C.
6. Add 5 mls of a 1000 ppm solution of potassium nitrate to petri dish D.

RESULTS:

1. After 1 week carefully record the number of seeds which germinated and calculate the germination percentage.

NAME _____

LAB SECTION _____

DATA SUMMARY

Treatment	Number of Seeds Germinated	% Germination
A. Distilled Water Control		
B. 1000 ppm Gibberellic Acid		
C. 5000 ppm Thiourea		
D. 1000 ppm Potassium Nitrate		

DATA EVALUATION

1. Prepare a bar graph based on your results from this experiment. Plot the percent germination values.

   A) Comparison of various growth regulators on the percent germination of 'Grand Rapids' lettuce seed.

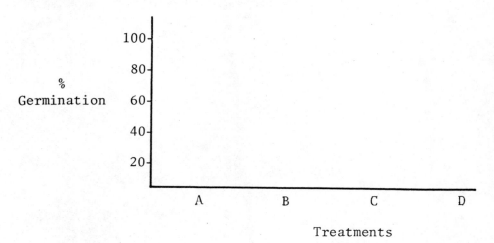

THOUGHT PROVOKERS

1. How might each of the chemicals used in this experiment be used commercially to enhance germination?

2. Will the application of any of these chemicals overcome dormancy caused by immature embryos? Explain!

3. What types of dormancy might GA, cytokinins, thiourea and KNO_3 overcome?

Seed Testing

Seed testing for percent germination and viability is a vital part of plant propagation. It is a means of evaluating seed quality and a means of ultimately determining the quantity of seeds needed per unit of planting area.

When testing for seed viability, the first test which comes to mind is germination percentage, which is the number of normal seedlings produced from a given lot of pure seed. In general, it is advisable when determining the germination percentage to use 4 lots of 100 seeds each. If any 2 of the lots differ by more than 10% germination, another test should be seriously considered. The average of the 4 lots thus becomes the germination percentage.

In germination testing, the seeds are usually placed under optimum light and temperature conditions in growth chambers. Containers such as plastic boxes, and covered petri dishes are useful as germinators. Media used in germination containers include paper blotters, filter paper, absorbent cotton or tissue, paper towelling, sand, soil or vermiculite.

Another method for seed testing is the rolled towel test or rag doll test. To use this technique, paper towelling (germination blotters or cloth can be substituted for the towels) is moistened with water and the seeds are placed along one side so that the edge of the towel can be turned over to cover the seeds. More rows of seed can be spaced along the towel as it is rolled up, with the seeds inside. The rolled towels should not be tightly wrapped, and should be placed either horizontally or vertically into germination trays.

When testing the germination of tree and shrub seeds, it is often done by sowing the seeds in flats of sterile sand and placing them in greenhouses for a predetermined period. For many woody plant seeds this period may be from 10 to 14 days, but can last up to 4 months for slow-germinating seeds.

In addition to germination tests, several other methods can and often are used to evaluate seed viability. The tetrazolium test is a biochemical measure of viability which is determined by the formation of a red color in the embryo of seeds soaked in a 0.1 to 1.0% solution of 2,3,5-triphenyltetrazolium chloride (TTC). In the presence of living tissue the TTC is reduced to triphenyl formazan which produces the red staining of the embryo, while non-living tissues remain unstained or colorless. Results can be obtained from this test within 1 hour.

The malachite green test is similar to the TTC test for viability. This is also a biochemical means to measure viability. Seeds are soaked in a 0.004% solution of malachite green for 24 hours. The living tissues (those respiring) will convert the malachite green to the colorless leucomalachite, while the remaining non-living will remain green.

The excised embryo is an alternative method for measuring the approximate seed germination percentage, which can be a time saving technique for many dormant seeds. An approximate value of dormant seeds can be obtained in 2-15 days or sooner, if necessary. Using conventional germination, a similar determination of germination percentage may take up to 6 months or even more if a stratification period is required. To perform this test, it is necessary only to remove or excise the embryo from the remainder of the seeds and germinate it alone. Properly done, a viable embryo will either germinate or show some signs of activity such as spreading of the cotyledons or development of chlorophyll, while a nonviable embryo will become discolored, soft, moldy and will fail to germinate. The rapidity with which these signs appear may be an indication of the seed vigor.

The actual excision must be done carefully to avoid damaging the embryo. In cases of hard seed, it will be necessary to scarify and soak the seed for 1-4 days in water prior to the actual excision operation in order to soften the seed coat. The seed coats are removed with a sharp knife or surgeon's scalpel and the embryo then carefully removed. If an endosperm is present, it is often advisable to float the split seed on water for 1/2 to 1 hour and the embryo can be removed more easily.

Once excised, the embryos are treated in much the same manner that one would treat whole germinating seeds. Placing them on moist filter paper in petri dishes is a common practice. The petri dishes are kept in the light at a temperature of 18-23°C (64-74°F) in a growth chamber for a period of 3 days to several weeks depending upon the embryos.

SELECTED REFERENCE MATERIALS

Barton, L. V. 1953. Seed storage and viability. Contr. Boyce Thompson Inst. 17:87-103.

Bonner, F. T. 1974. Seed testing In Seeds of woody plants in the United States, Agri. Handbook 450, pp. 136-152. U.S. Dept. Agri. For. Service, Washington, D.C.

Heit, C. E. 1955. The excised embryo method for testing germination quality of dormant seed. Proc. Assoc. Off. Seed Anal. 45:108-117.

Lakon, G. 1949. The topographical tetrazolium method for determining the germination capacity of seeds. Plant Physiol. 24:389-394.

Parker, J. 1953. New methods for the determination of forest tree seed germinability. J. Forestry 51:34.

LABORATORY PROJECT XXVII. TESTING FOR SEED VIABILITY AND GERMINATION.

PURPOSE:
     To compare various methods of testing seed viability and germination and to contrast the difference between seeds which are viable and those which will germinate.

PART I: TRIPHENYLTETRAZOLIUM TEST - TTC

MATERIALS:
     Pre-soaked corn (Zea mays), bean (Phaseolus sp.) or other suitable
          seeds
     Petri dishes
     Grease pencil
     Filter paper
     Razor blade
     2,3,5-triphenyltetrazolium chloride (TTC) - 0.10% solution

PROCEDURE:
     1. Using a grease pencil, label the tops of 2 petri dishes with your
        name and the treatment.
             Treatments
                Lot A
                Lot B
     2. Place 1 piece of filter paper in the bottom of each petri dish.
     3. Select 10 seeds from both lots.
     4. Cut the seeds longitudinally through the center of the embryo with a
        razor blade.
     5. Place half of each seed on the filter paper in the appropriate petri
        dish and discard the other half.
     6. Immerse the seeds in the TTC solution and replace the cover.

RESULTS:
     1. After 1/2 hour visually examine the two lots of seeds and record your
        results.

DATA SUMMARY

TRIPHENYLTETRAZOLIUM CHLORIDE TEST

Treatment (Lot)	Number of Seeds Per Lot	Number of Viable Seeds	% Viable Seeds
A			
B			

235

PART II: PETRI DISH GERMINATION TEST

MATERIALS:
  Pre-soaked corn (Zea mays), bean (Phaseolus sp.) or other suitable
    seeds of 2 ages or stored under 2 different temperature regimes
  Petri dishes
  Grease pencil
  Filter paper
  Distilled water
  Seed germinator

PROCEDURE:
  1. Using a grease pencil, label the tops of 2 petri dishes with your
     name, the date, and the treatment.
       Treatments
         Lot A
         Lot B
  2. Place 2 pieces of filter paper in the bottom of each petri dish.
  3. Pour distilled water into the petri dishes and allow the filter paper
     to become saturated.
  4. After 10 minutes pour off the excess water.
  5. Select 10 seeds from both lots.
  6. Place the seeds (uncut) into the appropriate petri dish.
  7. Set both petri dishes in the seed germinator.

RESULTS:
  1. Record your results after 3, 5 and 7 days.

DATA SUMMARY

PETRI DISH GERMINATION TEST

Treatment (Lot)	Number of Seeds Per Lot	Number of Seeds Germinated			% Germination		
		Day 3	Day 5	Day 7	Day 3	Day 5	Day 7
A							
B							

236

PART III: ROLLED TOWEL OR RAG DOLL TEST

MATERIALS:

  Two different lots of pre-soaked corn (Zea mays), bean (Phaseolus sp.)
      or other suitable seeds
  Tags
  Pencil
  Paper towels
  Beakers
  Shallow pan
  Distilled water
  Seed germinator

PROCEDURE:

1. Print a tag for each treatment.

   Treatments
        Lot A
        Lot B
2. Saturate 2 paper towels with distilled water in a shallow pan.
3. Select 10 seeds from both lots.
4. Place each lot of seeds equally spaced in the center half of the
   paper towels.
5. Roll up the towels (left to right) with the seeds inside.
6. Secure the appropriate tags around the rolls.
7. Place the rolls in a beaker containing 2 cm of water in the seed
   germinator.

RESULTS:

1. Record your results after 3, 5 and 7 days.

DATA SUMMARY

ROLLED TOWEL TEST

Treatment (Lot)	Number of Seeds Per Lot	Number of Seeds Germinated			% Germination		
		Day 3	Day 5	Day 7	Day 3	Day 5	Day 7
A							
B							

PART IV: SOIL GERMINATION TEST

MATERIALS:
        Two different lots of pre-soaked corn (<u>Zea</u> <u>mays</u>), bean (<u>Phaseolus</u> sp.)
          or other suitable material
        Labels
        Pencil
        Propagation medium in flats

PROCEDURE:
        1. Print a label for each treatment.
                <u>Treatments</u>
                    Lot A
                    Lot B
        2. Select 10 uniform seeds from both lots.
        3. Plant the seeds in rows and place the flat in the greenhouse.

RESULTS:
        1. After 7 days, record your results.

DATA SUMMARY

SOIL GERMINATION TEST

Treatment (Lot)	Number of Seeds Per Lot	Number of Seeds Germinated	% Germination
A			
B			

THOUGHT PROVOKERS

1. Contrast the terms <u>viability</u> and <u>germination</u>.

2. Which lot of seeds (Lot A or Lot B) is more desirable? Why?

3. What does the Tetrazolium Test actually measure?

4. What significant role does the embryo play in the Tetrazolium Test?

5. Which of the seed testing techniques do you think is best? Why?

Seed Sowing

Growing plants from seed is the most universal method of propagation. All horticulturists, both amateur and professional, have at one time or another sown seed to grow plants. When preparing to grow plants from seeds, remembering a few simple procedures will save time and wasted effort, and help to bring success.

MEDIA

Provided you start with good seed, requirements for germination are rather simple; a moist medium (well-drained and well-aerated), plus a favorable temperature. Many horticulturists follow a practice of mixing the medium used for sowing seed with equal proportions of soil plus sand and/or peat. A number of commercially prepared materials are readily available.

Soil or sand can be used alone with success while other commonly used media include perlite, vermiculite, peat, or sphagnum moss alone or in various combinations.

Seeds which are very small such as petunias, should be sown on a medium which has been screened to give a fine-textured seeding surface.

CONTAINERS

Where small quantities of seed are to be sown, a simple method is to use a clay or plastic pot. The shallow types are preferred. Place some drainage material in the bottom of the container (broken pot chips). The seeding medium is placed in the container, with the rough pieces screened out and a finer surface screened on top.

Where large quantities of seed are sown a simple container to use is a wooden or plastic flat. These must be constructed in such a way that drainage is provided, either through spaces between the bottom boards in the case of wooden flats, or holes in plastic flats.

For the homeowner, the bottom half of a waxed milk carton with holes punched in the bottom will make a suitable make-shift container for starting and growing plants.

SEED FLAT PREPARATION

Fill the container or flat with the medium to be used for seed germination and using a board or similar object, gently firm the medium in the container to about 1 cm (0.5 in) from the top avoiding the elimination of pore spaces necessary for aeration. Water the compressed medium evenly so that the water is distributed throughout. Let the flat drain for a few hours before proceeding with the seed sowing operation.

SOWING SEEDS
Seeds may be broadcast over the surface of the soil or may be sown in rows. Very fine seeds, i.e., petunias, begonias and snapdragons are sometimes broadcast over the surface of the soil but sowing in rows is preferred. Larger seeds are more conventionally sown in rows.

After seeds have been carefully sown, cover lightly with the growing medium. Fine seeds are usually not covered, but are watered lightly with a fine mist which will wash them down into the medium. As a general rule of thumb, the best way to judge depth for planting is to plant the seed to a depth about 2 to 3 times its diameter. Thus for fine seeds a thin covering or no covering will suffice.

When sowing seeds, be careful not to sow too thickly. Crowded seedlings grow rapidly, but become tall and spindly making them less desirable. In addition, seeds should not be sown thickly as this increases the chances of the occurrence of the fungal disease damping-off. Damping-off is a disease of seedlings that grows at or near the soil surface, causing the young plants to rot. Use of a pasteurized or "sterile" soil helps to prevent this problem. As a further precaution against damping-off, seed and soil can be treated with fungicides, but good cultural practices, i.e., light, watering and good air drainage, will usually help in preventing this problem.

WATERING
Watering is one of the chief reasons for success or failure with seedlings. The soil should be moist, but not wet, at the time of planting, and it should be kept as near as possible to this state at all times. Small seedlings dry out very quickly - and once is often fatal!

On the other hand, roots must have oxygen as well as water, and if the soil is kept soaked for very long the plants literally drown. There are no set rules for the time to water - the condition of the soil determines whether to water or not.

CARE OF THE SEED FLAT
Once the seeds have been sown, it is imperative that the flat be kept from drying out excessively. Quite commonly this can be prevented by covering the flat with a piece of glass or clear plastic. In addition, this practice not only helps to reduce watering but aids in maintaining constant environmental conditions necessary for rapid, uniform germination.

Water the seed flat only when the soil has visibly begun to dry out. Overwatering may lead to numerous disease problems which ultimately result in seedling losses. If overwatering leads to damping-off, prepare a fungicide drench and wet the soil thoroughly.

242

TRANSPLANTING

When the first true leaves (which are more or less typical of the later leaves) appear, the seedlings can be transplanted. Most seedlings when first germinated, have 2 small "seed leaves" or cotyledons. When the first true leaves are visible it is the best time to transplant. The transplanting operation temporarily checks the growth of the seedlings, making them grow into more compact plants. The seedlings are lifted, a few at a time, from the seed flat with a pencil or small, flat stick (a pot label is good), and planted one by one in larger containers.

To handle without damaging, the tiny plants should be held by a leaf (not the stem) between the thumb and forefinger (Figure 36). Holes of appropriate depth and about 5 cm (2 in) apart are made in the medium of the new container and the seedlings are inserted in these.

Roots should not be exposed to the air any longer than necessary. After the seedling is inserted in a hole, the medium should be gently firmed about the roots.

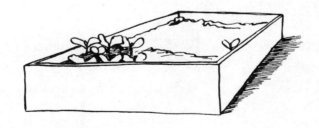

FIGURE 36.   TRANSPLANTING SEEDLINGS.

NOTES

244

LABORATORY PROJECT XXVIII. SEED SOWING.

PURPOSE:
To demonstrate the art of sowing seeds using both the broadcast and row methods.

MATERIALS:
Seed packages
Containers for sowing
Germination medium
Labels
Pencil
Mist sprayer
Fine quartz sand
50 ml beaker
(Optional: panes of glass or plastic)

PROCEDURE:
1. Select the seeds to be sown. Choose at least one type which has small seeds (i.e., petunia, begonia).
2. Read the seed package for germination information.
3. Print a label for each type of seed to be sown.
4. Fill the sowing containers with the medium and firm it gently.
5. Sow the seeds.
   A. Row Method
      i. Using a wooden label, make several rows about 1 cm (0.5 in) deep and 4 cm (1.5 in) apart.
      ii. Thinly sprinkle the seeds in the labeled rows.
      iii. Cover the seeds with the germination medium.
   B. Broadcast Method
      i. Pour about 1 cm (0.5 in) of fine quartz sand into the 50 ml beaker and incorporate some of the small seeds into it. (Do not pour the entire package of seeds into the sand. The quantity may appear minute, but there is actually a large amount of seeds per package.)
      ii. Evenly broadcast the sand-seed mixture by gently sprinkling it onto the medium in one of the containers. Do not cover the seeds with more medium.
6. After sowing, water the seeds in well with the mist sprayer. The medium should be moist but the seeds undisturbed.
7. Place the containers under mist. (Optional: Cover them with a pane of glass or plastic and place out of direct sunlight.)

RESULTS:
1. Observe the containers daily, noting which seeds germinated first.
2. Transplant the seedlings.

NOTES

THOUGHT PROVOKERS

1. Why should seeds be thinly sown?

2. What would be the advantage of using the row method of sowing seeds in regard to disease control?

3. When using a piece of glass or plastic to cover the seed flat, why should it not be placed in direct sunlight?

Propagation of Specialized Stems

Most plants, in one fashion or another, reproduce themselves. While this may be largely via a sexual process, many plants have adapted mechanisms which allow them to naturally reproduce themselves in an asexual manner. In addition, some plants have adapted very specialized parts that are used in the reproductive process. These specialized structures include the bulb, corm, tuber, tuberous root, rhizome, stolon and runner.

BULBS

Bulbs consist of a growing point surrounded by layers of fleshy leaf bases which are attached to a compact stem called the basal plate. Bulbs are most commonly classified as tunicate or non-tunicate. The onion, hyacinth, squill, amaryllis, snowdrop, tulip and daffodil are examples of tunicate or nonscaly bulbs, which have the fleshy leaf bases arranged in concentric layers around the growing point. These bulbs are called tunicate because the outer layer of leaves dry and form a protective "tunic" covering the bulb.

The lily is an example of a non-tunicate or scaly bulb. The fleshy leaf bases that compose the lily bulb overlap each other resulting in a scaly appearance. Scaly bulbs do not have a protective tunic and as a result are more easily damaged and susceptible to dessication if improperly stored.

PROPAGATION OF TUNICATE BULBS

There are a great number of ways that tunicate bulbs can be propagated. The simplest method to produce more plants from tunicate bulbs is by offsets. Offsets are small bulbs that form naturally at the base of the parent bulb. When a bulb is dug, the offsets are separated and planted to produce new plants. Small offsets will usually produce only vegetative growth the first few years after separation, depending on species.

In a number of bulbous crops, most notably the hyacinth, offsets are not readily produced, so artificial stimulation by scooping, scoring, coring or sectioning is used to induce new bulb formation. Scooping involves removal of the entire basal plate, so that when done properly, it will remove the shoot and flower bud at the center of the bulb and expose the fleshy leaf bases. Small bulblets will initiate and begin to develop at these locations (Figure 37).

249

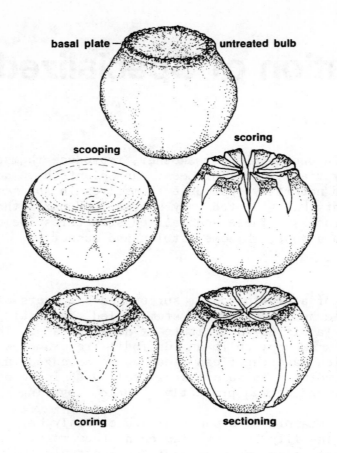

basal plate — untreated bulb

scooping

scoring

coring

sectioning

FIGURE 37. METHODS OF PROPAGATING BULBS, BY SCOOPING,
SCORING, CORING AND SECTIONING.

Following scooping, the bulbs should be dipped in a fungicide to protect the cut surface and then placed in a warm (21°C/70°F) dark location for approximately 2 weeks, thus allowing the bulb to dry and form wound tissues on the cut surfaces. When the scales begin to swell (usually during the 3rd week), the temperature should be increased to 30°C (85°F) with a relative humidity of approximately 85%. The new bulblets will be ready for planting when new roots form.

The first year, the scooped bulb and attached bulblets are planted while still attached in loose well-drained soil, about 2 to 3 cm (0.75-1.25 in) deep. During the first year, the bulblets will produce only foliage. After the foliage has turned yellow and begins to dry, the bulbs and bulblets can be dug. While scooping will produce as many as 25 to 50 bulblets per mother bulb, they will still be quite small and will require an additional 4-5 years of growth before attaining sufficient size to flower.

When scoring a bulb, 3 V-shaped cuts are made through the basal plate, so that there are 6 pie-shaped sections (Figure 37). These cuts are made deep enough to destroy the main growing shoot and to reach just below the widest point of the bulb. After scoring, the bulbs are dipped in a fungicide, and buried upside-down in clean dry sand at a depth of approximately 5 cm (2 in). After wound tissues are formed on the cut surfaces, remove the bulbs from the sand and treat them the same as scooped bulbs. Scoring will produce about 12-25 bulblets per mother bulb, but they will be larger and should flower in approximately 3-4 years.

When coring, one removes the center portion of the basal plate and the main growing point of the bulb (Figure 37). Cored bulbs are treated the same as scooped bulbs; however, they tend to produce fewer but larger bulblets, that reach flowering size in 2-3 years.

Some bulb growers propagate bulbs by the process of sectioning (Figure 37). Sectioning involves cutting the bulb into 5-10 pie-shaped vertical sections, each with a piece of basal plate at its base. Bulblets form at the basal plate of each cutting.

PROPAGATION OF SCALY BULBS
Like tunicate bulbs, scaly bulbs are easily propagated by offsets, how-ever, they are usually produced too slowly to be of much value as a commercial procedure.

Scaly bulbs are most often propagated by removing the healthy outer scales from the bulb and planting them one-half their length in a rooting medium (Figure 38). In the process of scaling, bulbs to be used are dried

FIGURE 38. SCALING LILY BULBS.

after flowering, the scales removed and planted in rows about 2 to 3 cm (1 in) apart. New bulblets will form at the base of the scales in a few months, at which time they can be field planted. The mother bulbs, from which the scales were obtained, can be replanted, and they will regenerate more scales which can be used for additional propagation in 1-2 years.

Some lilies produce aerial bulbs, called bulbils, in the axils of the leaves during the summer, usually after flowering. These bulbils can be used to produce new plants by removing them from the parent plant and growing them for a period of 2-3 years, at which time they should be of flowering size. Bulbils can be induced in some lilies by removing the flower buds from the plant.

CORMS

Corms are the swollen bases of flowering stems, enclosed by a few thin tunic-like leaves beneath which is a solid core of stem tissue. In contrast to the bulb, which is predominantly fleshy leaf bases, the corm is a solid piece of stem tissue with clearly defined nodes and internodes. The gladiolus, freesia, and crocus are examples of cormous plants.

PROPAGATION OF CORMS

Plants which grow from corms naturally produce new corms or cormels at the base of each shoot every year. The old corm is used up producing the plant and the plant then produces a new corm. In general more than one flowering shoot may grow from a large corm, and as a result 2 corms of smaller size will form from the original corm.

Small corms, or cormels, are formed at the base of the new corm. These cormels can be separated from the parent corm, planted in a well-drained soil, and they will flower in 1-3 years.

TUBERS

Tubers are composed of stem tissue which has enlarged into an underground storage organ. Probably the best example of a tuber is the Irish potato, but both the caladium and the Jerusalem artichoke are also tubers. In the potato, the "eyes" are actually buds and will form the stems of the new plant.

PROPAGATION OF TUBERS

Tuberous plants can be propagated by cutting the tuber into sections so that each "seed piece" has an "eye" or bud. Each of these pieces should weigh 28-57 g (1-2 oz) so they can provide sufficient stored food while the new plant becomes established. After cutting into "seed pieces", the sections should be allowed to dry and suberize or form a new skin-like layer. In addition, treatment with a fungicide will help prevent the "seed piece" from decaying before the new plant forms.

TUBEROUS ROOTS

Tuberous roots are often confused with tubers, however, they are actually root tissue and do not have "eyes" or buds as tubers do. Plants which produce tuberous roots include the sweet potato, dahlia, gloxinia, tuberous begonia, bleeding heart, wind flower (Anemone), and cyclamen.

PROPAGATION OF TUBEROUS ROOTS

The tuberous root such as the dahlia is propagated by including a section of the crown or stem with a bud, so that a new plant will be produced. If one fails to provide a piece of stem tissue with the tuberous root, no shoot system will develop (Figure 39).

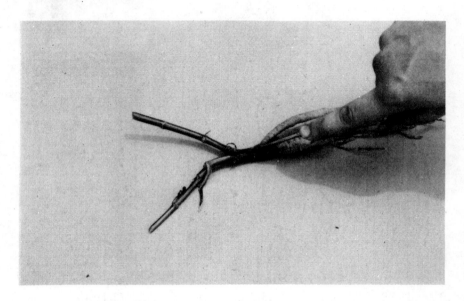

FIGURE 39. DIVIDING DAHLIA ROOTS.

With sweet potatoes, it is not necessary to include a portion of stem or crown tissue, as they will produce adventitious shoots directly from the tuberous root. These shoots called "slips", then form adventitious roots and the young plants are then separated and planted.

Some plants such as the gloxinia and tuberous begonia have tuberous roots or enlarged stems located between the regular stem and the roots. These tuberous structures enlarge each year and can be propagated by cutting them into pie-shaped sections so that each section includes a bud. A fungicide should be applied to the sections to prevent decay and the sections should be allowed to dry prior to planting.

RHIZOMES

A rhizome is a modified stem in which the main axis of the plant grows horizontally at or just below the soil surface.

The German or bearded iris, Lily-of-the-valley, bamboo, banana, sugar cane and many members of the grass family reproduce _via_ the rhizome.

PROPAGATION OF RHIZOMES

Plants which have rhizomes are usually propagated by division of the plant. In most cases the rhizome contains shoot buds and can be propagated by cutting it into sections, so that each contains at least one bud (Figure 40).

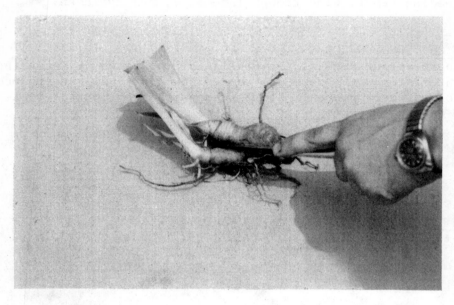

FIGURE 40. DIVIDING GERMAN IRIS VIA RHIZOMES.

SELECTED REFERENCE MATERIALS

Ball, V. (ed.). 1972. The Ball Red Book, 12th ed., Chicago: Geo. J. Ball, Inc.

Crockett, J. V. 1971. Bulbs. Time-Life Books, New York, N.Y.

Guse, W. E. and F. E. Larson. 1976. Propagation from bulbs, corms, tubers, rhizomes and tuberous roots and stems. Pacific Northwest Cooperative Ext. Pub. 164. pp. 8.

LABORATORY PROJECT XXIX.   PROPAGATION OF SPECIALIZED STEMS.

PURPOSE:
    To demonstrate the methods used to propagate various plants which have
specialized stems, i.e., rhizomes, bulbs, corms, tubers, and tuberous roots.

MATERIALS:
    Propagation knife
    Pruning shears
    Labels
    Pencil
    Propagation medium in flats
    Bulbs - tulips, daffodils, lilies, hyacinths
    Corms - gladiolus, crocus
    Tuberous roots - dahlia, sweet potato
    Tubers - Irish potato
    Rhizomes - German iris, canna lily

PROCEDURE:
    1. For this exercise, prepare examples of each of the following types
       of propagation.
            Sectioning bulbs
            Scoring bulbs (or scooping)
            Separating offsets ("slabs", "splits" or "spoons" of daffodils or
                other narcissus)
            Division of rhizomes
            Scaling bulbs
            Division of tuberous roots
            Division of tubers

NOTES

THOUGHT PROVOKERS

1. What is the difference between a tuber and a tuberous root?

2. Why might a hyacinth breeder choose to "scoop" bulbs rather than wait for offsets?

3. How might tissue culture render techinques like scooping and scaling bulbs obsolete?

LABORATORY PROJECT XXX.   PRODUCTION OF TUBERS FROM LEAF-BUD CUTTINGS.

PURPOSE:
   To illustrate the production of tubers from leaf-bud cuttings. (Note: This method is of great value to potato breeders.)

MATERIALS:
   Healthy potato (Solanum tuberosum) plants.
   Sharp knife
   Deep flats or packs
   Sterile sand
   Labels
   Pencil

PROCEDURE:
   1. Select healthy stems and make mallet-type leaf-bud cuttings by cutting the stems approximately 1 cm (0.4 in) above and 1 cm (0.4 in) below each node. Each cutting will thus have a leaf attached to a 2 cm (0.7 in) stem segment with a bud present in the leaf axil.
   2. Fill the flat or other container with sterile sand.
   3. Place the stem segment horizontally in the sterile sand, covering the entire stem segment and bud to a depth of 2 cm (0.7 in).
   4. Label and water well.
   5. Place flats containing cuttings in a greenhouse of 21°C (70°F) day temperature.

RESULTS:
   1. Observe the development of the tubers in the leaf axils after 3 weeks.

REFERENCE:
   Lauer, F. I. 1977. Tubers from leaf-bud cuttings: a tool for potato seed certification and breeding programs. Amer. Potato J. 54:457-464.

THOUGHT PROVOKERS

1. Where do potato tubers normally form?

2. What may have caused the axillary bud to form a tuber?

3. Of what use is this technique to a plant breeder?

LABORATORY PROJECT XXXI.   PROPAGATION OF LILIES BY SCALING.

PURPOSE:
   To demonstrate the ease of propagating lilies by bulblet production from bulb scales and to compare effects of various media on bulblet production.

MATERIALS:
   Healthy lily (Lilium sp.) bulbs
   Sphagnum peat, vermiculite, perlite and sterile sand
   Flats or cell-paks
   Labels
   Pencils
   1-quart size polyethylene bags (Alternative Procedure)
   Twist-ties or rubber bands (Alternative Procedure)

PROCEDURE:
   1. Remove all dried, damaged and thin outer scales.
   2. Select several plump firm large scales.
   3. Place the various media in packs or flats.
   4. Place the basal 1/3 to 1/2 of the scales at a slight angle from the vertical in each medium to be tested.
   5. Label, water well and place in a 21°C (70°F) greenhouse or in a location of similar temperature.
   6. Observe the scales at 1-week intervals and record in the Data Summary.

ALTERNATIVE PROCEDURE:
   1 & 2. Same as above.
   3. Place the selected media in the polyethylene bags, filling 1/2 to 2/3 full.
   4. Moisten medium and pour off excess water.
   5. Place the scales in each medium to 1/2 their length.
   6. Label, close bag with twist-ties or rubber band and leave at room temperature.
   7. Observe the scales at 1-week intervals and record in the Data Summary.

RESULTS:
   1. Record your observations of bulblet formation from the scales in the Data Summary.

DATA SUMMARY

Medium	First Week	Second Week	Third Week	Fourth Week	Fifth Week
Sphagnum Peat					
Vermiculite					
Perlite					
Sand					

Additional observations:

264

THOUGHT PROVOKERS

1. What do you think stimulated the formation of the bulblets?

2. What are intercalary meristems? How might they relate to bulblet formation on bulb scales?

3. Based on results similar to yours, if you were attempting to increase a bulb of a new introduction, how many-fold an increase might you expect if the outer 20 scales were used?

Propagation By Tissue Culture

The propagation of greenhouse plants by tissue culture is likely to be one of the methods that propagation specialists will be using for many species in the near future. Although biologists have used tissue culture for fundamental studies in plant metabolism and differentiation and breeders are beginning to produce haploid plants from pollen grains for the eventual development of homozygous diploid plants for breeding work, the technique of tissue culture as a propagation tool has only recently been developed. Its commercial applications are even more recent.

Tissue culture is of obvious value to the commercial grower, but it is of equal importance to the plant breeder. It can be employed on problems not amenable to conventional approaches or on those that would be more effectively attacked with unconventional methods such as:

1. Broadening the genetic base by increasing genetic diversity. This can be accomplished in the fusion of cells from different species with the resultant hybrid leading to increased genetic diversity. This is particularly applicable in situations where abnormal endosperm development results in the failure of seed formation.
2. Transmission of heterozygosity and epistasis from parent to offspring. Normally, only additive genetic variance is transmitted through the gametes. Intralocus and interlocus interactions (nonadditive genetic variance) are not transmitted.
3. Storage of germplasm. Where asexual propagation does occur, tissue culture provides a method of maintaining valuable genotypes and preserving diversity.
4. Exchange of germplasm. This would also have the advantages of chromosome stability in the culture of disease-free material.
5. Clonal propagation for rapid multiplication of uniform superior genotypes.
6. Selection for disease resistance in vitro by using pathogenic toxins.
7. Selection for improved nutritional characteristics.
8. Somatic breeding and, where the sexual cycle allows for excessive recombination in some high polyploids or in asexually reproducing plants, somatic cell selection of variants due to chromosome substitution.

Many other uses for tissue culture are being employed and devised in the field of plant breeding.

Tissue culture means the production of a new plant by growing a very small piece of plant material in aseptic conditions, usually in a test tube

267

or flask, in nutrient medium. The medium may be liquid or solidified with agar. The liquid or suspension cultures have to be aerated and this is usually done by rotating or agitating the flasks. The technique has been known for some time and has been used commercially for the propagation of orchids since the 1920's when Knudson devised a suitable medium for the germination of orchid seeds and the growth of seedlings. Orchid seeds have no endosperm, a tissue which provides food for the embryos of most seeds. Consequently, in nature, unless they germinate in symbiotic association with some other plant, the embryos die. On nutrient agar orchid seeds germinate and the young plants flourish. Tissue culture has also been used for the production of virus-free plants, usually following heat therapy. Virus-free chrysanthemums and strawberries, for example, can be produced from meristems excised from rapidly growing shoots of plants grown at very high temperatures. The plants are grown in controlled atmosphere chambers in which the temperature is gradually increased to 38 to 41°C, under optimum conditions of light and moisture. The mother plants suffer from such treatment but the meristems are also virus-free. The meristems grow into mother plants, usually needed to produce stock plants from which cuttings are taken for sale. These are all grown in as sanitary conditions as possible and isolated from possible recontamination particularly from insects which are virus vectors. Meristems, which are very small pieces of tissue, are difficult to establish and grow, hence for propagation purposes, if there is not immediate concern for viruses, somewhat larger pieces of tissue called shoot tips are used.

Quite recently, methods of rapid clonal propagation of gerbera, asparagus, chrysanthemum and Boston fern have been developed. Commercially gerbera plants, for example, have been propagated by seed but as they are extremely heterozygous, the seedlings are not homogeneous. Although efforts have been made to select fairly uniform plants, some heterozygosity is found in all strains, not only in different flower colors, but also in floral morphology, rapidity of growth and flowering and productivity. Gerbera can be propagated vegetatively by division of the mother plants but this is much too slow for commercial propagation as only a 50 to 100-fold increase per year of a selected plant is possible.

Murashige and his co-workers at the University of California have recently outlined a production system for the rapid clonal multiplication of gerbera using tissue culture. Greenhouse plants were separated into divisions which were stripped of all leaves until only a bud piece was left from which the shoot tips were excised. The shoot tips were disinfected with dilute laundry bleach and grown on agar containing a Murashige-Skoog nutrient formula. This contained the required mineral nutrients, such as nitrogen, phosphorus, potash, manganese, boron, iron, magnesium, etc., as well as the growth regulators, kinetin and indoleacetic acid, and vitamins and sucrose. The shoot tips proliferated to form many shoots or divisions but these had to be transferred to another medium for root formation before the little plants could be planted in soil. The test tubes or bottles containing the explants were maintained at a constant 27°C and 16 hours daily illumination with 1,000 lux Gro Lux light. The number of shoots could be multiplied 6-fold in four weeks when they were transferred to a nutrient medium containing no kinetin and relatively high concentrations of indoleacetic acid. The light intensity was increased to 10,000 lux by using cool white fluorescent lamps instead of the Gro Lux lamps. Roots formed on these explants in about two weeks, and then they could be transplanted into soil. These researchers have estimated a million-fold increase in gerbera plants, starting with one plant, in a one-year period.

Earle and Langhans at Cornell University have developed a similar procedure for the rapid clonal multiplication of chrysanthemums. Shoot tips were removed from plants growing under long day conditions in the greenhouse. These were placed in vials on agar containing a nutrient medium consisting of the Murashige-Skoog organic constituents, sucrose, vitamins and the growth regulators, naphthaleneacetic acid, kinetin and gibberellic acid. These were maintained at $24^{o}C$ under constant fluorescent light of 1,000 to 1,400 lux. High levels of NAA in relation to kinetin in the medium result in roots and callus on the explants whereas a reversal of these ratios results in leaf and shoot formation. It was therefore possible to obtain many shoots from one explant with high levels of kinetin and then to get these to root by moving them to a medium having relatively high levels of naphthalenacetic acid. Assumming the production of five shoots per explant every four weeks, excision and subculture of new shoot tips every four weeks, and two weeks for rooting, about 125 small plantlets would be produced in three months, 15,500 in six months and over 200 million in a year.

A slightly different technique was also developed at Cornell by the same horticulturists. By changing the composition of the culture medium they obtained callus from the explants which were then placed in a suspension medium, liquid nutrient medium without agar, in flasks on a culture wheel which rotated slowly. The movement of the flasks aerated the medium and also caused the callus to break up and proliferate. Pieces of this callus were, from time to time, transferred onto agar medium where plantlets formed. Earle and Langhans estimated that, although organization of plantlets from callus is slow during the first six months, the dramatic increase in production in the next six months would lead to the production of 90 billion 6-inch plants in a year.

These techniques sound like the answer to a plant propagator's prayer. Unfortunately there are still problems with tissue culture. Many species are not amenable to tissue culture or suitable techniques have not yet been determined for them. The proliferation of callus has often led to chromosomal damage, an increase in the number of gene mutations and the production of plants unlike the parent plant. Some species do not produce multiple shoots from a shoot tip. Indeed, this character differs from cultivar to cultivar within the same species as Earle and Langhans have shown in chrysanthemums. However, they also found few mutant plants produced from callus and these usually arose from cultivars known to be chimeras and subject to sporting under conventional methods of propagation.

The problem of aseptic conditions is one that must be considered very seriously in tissue culture. The minimum requirement is for an autoclave which can be of relatively simple construction if a source of steam is available. All instruments, media and containers must be sterilized in the autoclave. The placing of tissue in the containers is best done in a positive air flow transfer chamber, in which filtered air passes through the working area maintaining sterile conditions. Although contamination may be a problem initially a good technician will soon catch on to the tricks of the trade and little or no contamination is evident in a laboratory where tissue culture has been conducted for a while.

Another major problem is the determination of techniques for species not previously cultured. However, once the technique, which includes determining the best tissue to use, i.e., shoot tips, leaves, callus, etc., the appropriate medium and environmental conditions, and whether transferral from one type of medium to another is necessary, has been perfected, the production of plants from tissue culture becomes a routine matter.

HAPLOID PLANT CULTURE

The preparation of haploid plants proceeds along a tissue - callus (undifferentiated cells) - plantlet pathway rather than the shoot tip - plantlet method described before. The process of morphogenesis from undifferentiated cells may occur either by embryogenesis in the absence of exogenous hormones or by organogenesis induced by cytokinins. The first step in the preparation of haploids is the obtaining of immature pollen grains. In tomato, (Lycopersicon esculentum), flowers are removed from vigorously growing diploid plants at a bud length of 2-3 mm. This size normally corresponds to the stage of development where the pollen mother cells are in early meiosis. An aceto-orcein squash may be performed to determine the stage of meiotic division. The anthers are aseptically removed and cultured on a nutrient medium similar to the one previously described. Once the callus has developed and proliferated sufficiently it is recultured onto various different media. These media, in addition to a nutrient base, contain various levels of different cytokinins which induce differentiation of the callus into shoot and root tissue.

SELECTED REFERENCE MATERIAL

Ben-Jaacov, J. and R. W. Langhans. 1972. Rapid multiplication of chrysanthemum plants by stem-tip proliferation. HortScience 7:289-290.

Carlson, P. S. 1975. Meeting Report: Crop improvement techniques of plant cell and tissue culture. BioScience 25:747-749.

Daykin, M., R. W. Langhans and E. D. Earle. 1976. Tissue culture propagation of the double petunia. HortScience 11:35.

Earle, E. D. and R. W. Langhans. 1974. Propagation of chrysanthemum in vitro. I. Multiple plantlets from shoot tips and the establishment of tissue cultures. J. Amer. Soc. Hort. Sci. 99:128-132.

Earle, E. D. and R. W. Langhans. 1974. Propagation of chrysanthemum in vitro. II. Production, growth and flowering of plantlets from tissue cultures. J. Amer. Soc. Hort. Sci. 99:352-358.

Greshoff, P. M. and C. Doy. 1972. Development and differentiation of haploid Lycopersicon esculentum. Planta (Berl.) 107:161-171.

Hackett, W. P. 1969. The influence of auxin, catechol and methanolic tissue extracts on root initiation in aseptically cultured shoot apices of the juvenile and adult forms of Hedera helix. Proc. Inter. Plant Prop. Soc. 19:57-68.

Hackett, W. P. and J. M. Anderson. 1967. Aseptic multiplication and maintenance of differentiated carnation shoot tissue derived from shoot apices. Proc. Amer. Soc. Hort. Sci. 90:365-369.

Haramaki, C. 1971. Tissue culture of gloxinia. Proc. Inter. Plant Prop. Soc. 21:442-448.

Hill, G. P. 1968. Shoot formation in tissue cultures of chrysanthemum 'Bronze Pride'. Physiol. Planta. 21:386-389.

Jones, J. B. and T. Murashige. 1974. Tissue culture propagation of Aechmea fasciata Baker, and other Bromeliads. Proc. Inter. Plant Prop. Soc. 24:117-126.

Linsmaier, E. and F. Skoog. 1965. Organic growth factor requirements of tobacco tissue culture. Physiol. Planta. 18:100-127.

Morel, G. M. 1960. Producing virus-free cymbidiums. Amer. Orchid Soc. Bull. 29:495-497.

Murashige, T. 1966. Principles of in vitro culture. Proc. Inter. Plant Prop. Soc. 16:80-87.

Murashige, T. 1974. Plant propagation through tissue culture. Ann. Rev. Plant Physiol. 25:135-166.

Murashige, T., M. N. Shabde, P. M. Hasegawa, F. H. Takatori and J. B. Jones. 1972. Propagation of asparagus through shoot apex cultures. I. Nutrient medium for formation of plantlets. J. Amer. Soc. Hort. Sci. 97:158-161.

Murashige, T. and F. Skoog. 1962. A revised medium for rapid growth and bioassays with tobacco tissue cultures. Physiol. Planta. 15:473-497.

Nitsch, J. P. 1969. Plant propagation at a cellular level: a basis for future developments. Proc. Inter. Plant Prop. Soc. 19:123-132.

Nitsch, J. P. and C. Nitsch. 1969. Haploid plants from pollen grains. Science 163:85-87.

Reinert, R. A. and H. C. Mohr. 1967. Propagation of cattleya by tissue culture of lateral bud meristems. Proc. Amer. Soc. Hort. Sci. 91:664-671.

Sagawa, Y., T. Shoji and T. Shoji. 1966. Clonal propagation of cymbidiums through shoot tissue culture. Amer. Orchid Soc. Bull. 35:118-122.

Skirvin, R. M. and J. Janick. 1976. Tissue culture - induced variation in scented Pelargonium sp. J. Amer. Soc. Hort. Sci. 101:281-290.

Takatori, F. H., T. Murashige and J. I. Stillman. 1968. Vegetative propagation of asparagus through tissue cultures. HortScience 3:20-22.

White, P. R. 1963. The cultivation of animal and plant cells, 2 ed. New York; The Ronald Press Co.

NOTES

LABORATORY PROJECT XXXII.   MICROPROPAGATION OF CHRYSANTHEMUM.

PURPOSE:
    To demonstrate the basic techniques and principles involved in esta-
blishing tissue cultures and to illustrate the ability that plants possess
for generating callus tissue and new plantlets from shoot-tips.

MATERIALS:
    Chrysanthemum (C. morifolium) cuttings or other suitable materials
    Stock solutions
    Agar
    Sucrose
    Commercial NaOCl (Chlorox, Purex, etc.)
    Deionized water
    70% Ethanol
    1 oz French square bottles with tops, or other suitable containers
    Forceps
    Scalpel
    Beakers
    Grease pencils

Table 4.   Stock Solutions for Tissue Cultures.

Stock Solution Number	Component	Amount Grams/Liter	Milliliter per Liter of Medium	Concentration mg/Liter
1	NH_4NO_3	82.500	20	1,650
2	KNO_3	95.000	20	1,900
	H_3BO_3	1.240		6.2
	KH_2PO_4	34.000		170
3	KI	0.166	5	0.83
	$Na_2MoO_4 \cdot 2H_2O$	0.050		0.25
	$CoCl_2 \cdot 6H_2O$	0.005		0.25
4	$CaCl_2 \cdot 2H_2O$	88.000	5	444
	or			
	$CaCl_2$	66.420		440
5	$MgSO_4 \cdot 7H_2O$	74.000	5	370
	$MnSO_4 \cdot H_2O$	4.460		22.3
6	$ZnSO_4 \cdot 7H_2O$	1.720	5	8.6
	$CuSO_4 \cdot 5H_2O$	0.005		0.025
7	Na_2-EDTA	7.450	5	37.35
	$FeSO_4 \cdot 7H_2O$	5.570		27.85
8	Sucrose	30.000 gm/l	-	-
9	Bacto-agar	5.000 gm/l	-	-
10	Thiamine	-	-	0.4 mg/l
11	Inositol	-	-	100 mg/l
12	Kinetin	-	-	2 mg/l
13	NAA	-	-	0.02 mg/l

PROCEDURE:

1. After the stock solutions are mixed, bring to a volume of 1 liter with distilled water. The pH of the solution is adjusted to 5.5 with 0.1 N KOH or 0.1 N HCl.

2. Pour the medium to a depth of 2 cm in a French square bottle and autoclave at 15 lb/sq in at a temperature of 121°C for 20 minutes. If no autoclave is available, good results may be obtained with a pressure cooker. Distilled deionized water, beakers, and utensils should also be autoclaved at this time. Incubate the sterile cultures at room temperature for 1 week and check daily for contaminants.

3. Clean the surface of the transfer chamber or the laminar flow bench, using a 5% chlorox solution. This exercise can be attempted on a laboratory bench if no transfer chamber or laminar flow bench is available, but much attention must be given to maintaining asepsis.

4. Wash hands and arms up to the elbow with soap and water and dry with paper towelling. Wipe hands and arms with 70% alcohol just prior to beginning work at the transfer chamber or laminar flow bench.

5. The plant material you will attempt to culture must be sterile, otherwise contaminants will grow rapidly on the nutrient enriched medium. Soak in chlorox:water (1:10) solution for 10 minutes, then rinse in 3 rinses of sterile distilled deionized water.

6. Using sterile tools dipped in 70% alcohol and flamed, remove the leaves of the plant tissue until the tip of the stem is exposed.

7. Cut off the tip (Shoot-Tip Culture), which will include the apical meristem and a few immature leaves, and place it upright in the medium. Replace the lid on the French square bottle.

8. Place the culture with your name, date and laboratory section written with grease pencil on the bottle in the appropriate culture chamber.

9. POINTS TO REMEMBER
   A. When working on the laminar flow bench always keep your hands "down wind" from the objects or tissues you are working with in order to maintain sterile conditions.
   B. Always flame sterilize any tools used in the tissue culturing process, and please BE CAREFUL of the flame near the alcohol. Be prepared to act quickly if a fire should start.

NOTE TO INSTRUCTOR

It has been our practice to prepare all medium for laboratory projects XXXII and XXXIII one week prior to the laboratory period when they are to be used and to check regularly for contamination. In general, with large classes we have found it impractical for students to even prepare their own medium from stock solutions.

THOUGHT PROVOKERS

1. In those cultures where there was appreciable callus proliferation, did this increase in size result entirely from cell division or cell enlargement?

2. What do you see as the potential for tissue culture in Horticulture?

LABORATORY PROJECT XXXIII. ASEPTIC MICROPROPAGATION OF PETUNIA.

Aseptic micropropagation is the development of new plants in an artificial medium under aseptic conditions from very small pieces of plant. New roots and/or shoots or embryoids must develop to produce a new plant. Tissue culture, the maintenance of tissue or organs in aseptic culture, is also of great interest to the plant scientist.

In horticulture, aseptic techniques of micropropagation have been applied in the production of orchids, freesia, gladiolus, bromeliads, ferns, asparagus, and citrus. In plant breeding work tissue culture techniques have been used to rapidly increase selected lines or clones, e.g. in breeding of lilies. Virus free plants of some important clones of chrysanthemum, carnation, apple, cherry, and strawberry have been produced with the aid of aseptic culture.

Several types of media have been used for the culture of excised plant tissues. For research purposes it is necessary to use a well defined, reproducible medium. Many "recipes" for media have been proposed by workers in tissue culture, but the choice of medium will be affected by type of plant, type of tissue, and desired response of the explant.

PURPOSES:

To demonstrate the fundamental techniques of plant tissue culture and to contrast the effects of auxin-like and cytokinin-like growth regulators on the success of tissue cultures.

MATERIALS:

Petunia (Petunia hybrida) seedlings 4 to 6 weeks old
Commercial NaOCl (Chlorox, Purex, etc.)
95% Ethanol
Sterilized deionized distilled water
Disposable (or sterile) petri dishes or 1-ounce French square bottles
Forceps
Scalpels or new single-edge razor blades
Dissecting needles
Three 400 ml beakers
Masking tape or Parafilm
Media A, B, and C
Grease pencils

The media, which should be prepared in advance, are modified Linsmaier-Skoog media. Their composition is as follows:

Major Elements		mg/liter
Ammonium nitrate	NH_4NO_3	1650
Potassium nitrate	KNO_3	1900
Calcium chloride	$CaCl_2 \cdot 4H_2O$	440
Magnesium sulphate	$MgSO_4 \cdot 7H_2O$	370
Potassium dihydrogen phosphate	KH_2PO_4	170
Sodium EDTA	Na_2EDTA	37.3
Ferrous sulphate	$FeSO_4 \cdot 7H_2O$	27.8

Minor Elements		
Boric acid	H_3BO_3	6.2
Manganous sulphate	$MnSO_4 \cdot 4H_2O$	22.3
Zinc sulphate	$ZnSO_4 \cdot 4H_2O$	8.6
Potassium iodide	KI	0.83
Sodium molybdate	$Na_2MoO_4 \cdot 2H_2O$	0.25
Copper sulphate	$CuSO_4 \cdot 5H_2O$	0.025
Cobalt chloride	$CoCl_2 \cdot 6H_2O$	0.025

Organic Constituents	
Sucrose	25000
Agar (Difco Bacto)	7500
Thiamine	0.4
Myo-Inositol	100
Folic acid	0.5

In addition to the above, Medium A contains 0.5 mg/l Benzyladinine (BA) and Medium B contains 1.0 mg/l naphthalene acetic acid (NAA). Medium C (optional) contains both 0.5 mg/l BA and 1.0 mg/l NAA. All solutions are made with deionized distilled water.

The pH of these media was adjusted to 5.7-5.8 prior to the addition of the agar. After addition of the agar the media were autoclaved at 121°C for 20 minutes, then 25 ml poured into sterile petri dishes.

PROCEDURE:
Explants will be taken from sterile material and placed on the medium while working close to a flame. Hot air rising from the flame prevents 'drop-in' spores and contamination. All tools must be dipped in 95% ethanol and flamed prior to use.

PRECAUTIONS
1. 95% ETHANOL IS HIGHLY FLAMMABLE. ALWAYS OPERATE WITH EXTREME CARE IN THE VICINITY OF THE FLAME.
2. WASH HANDS AND WORKING SURFACES WITH 0.5% HYPOCHLORITE SOLUTION BEFORE MAKING TRANSFERS.

3. AVOID UNNECESSARY MOVEMENT AS THIS WILL CREATE EDDIES WHICH WILL BRING IN AIR-BORNE SPORES.
4. DIP AND FLAME INSTRUMENTS AFTER EVERY TRANSFER.

I.   From the plants provided, take 5 or 6 young expanding leaves and sterilize by immersion in 0.5% sodium hypochlorite solution for ten minutes. Working near the flame transfer to sterile distilled water for five minutes, repeat, then place in a sterile petri dish and cut into transverse sections of about 4 mm width. Flame your instruments before cutting the leaves.

II. Working near the flame, transfer 3 leaf pieces to each of 3 dishes of each medium. Make the transfers by using a dissecting needle and lift the cover of the petri dish only slightly and only when necessary.

III. Having made the transfers, place a piece of masking tape or parafilm around the dishes to prevent desiccation, label clearly, and place on a well-lighted lab bench or in a growth chamber. Observe your cultures after 1 week to check for contamination. After 2 weeks, look for signs of growth and record observations under "Data Summary". Check cultures at weekly intervals from then on.

RESULTS:
1. Record your observations in the data summary table each week. Note especially callus, shoot and root production; also observe contamination, if present. (If contamination occurs, describe it.)

DATA SUMMARY

Record your observations below.

	Week 1	Week 2	Week 3	Week 4	Week 5
Medium A					
Medium B					
Medium C					

THOUGHT PROVOKERS

1. What differences did you observe in the response of your explants in the three media used? How do you account for these responses?

2. Why do you think aseptic technique is important?

3. Suggest other additives for the media which may have a significant effect on the growth of the explant.

4. Why were the petri dishes sealed with parafilm?

5. Suggest procedures you might follow to make transplantable specimens from these growths.

APPENDIX I — GLOSSARY OF TERMS

ADVENTITIOUS: Buds, roots or stems appearing from other than regular places, e.g., buds arising from wounds, roots developing at the base of stems or stems developing from roots.

AFTER-RIPENING: Sum total of the physiological changes that take place within a seed after harvest so that germination can proceed.

ANNUAL: Plant which completes its life cycle in one season. A plant that grows from seed, and exhausts itself by flowering, producing seed, then dying, e.g., marigold, corn.

APICAL: Tip or apex, as the apical cell or apical meristem of a plant.

APOMIXIS: Formation of an embryo without fertilization.

ASEPTIC: Free of contamination or infection.

ASEXUAL REPRODUCTION: Development of new individual plants or animals without the union of gametes.

AUXIN: Hormone such as indoleacetic acid which controls or modifies growth.

AXILLARY BUDS: Buds produced where the leaf or petiole and stem intersect.

BENCH: 1. Table-like structure enclosed with boards on which potted plants are placed and grown or in which a medium is placed in order to encourage rooting of cuttings. 2. Table-like structure where grafting is sometimes done, "bench-grafting".

BLIND EYES: Buds which produce shoots which do not produce flowers.

BIENNIAL: Typically, a plant which grows vegetatively the first growing season, flowers and produces seed the second and then dies.

BOTTOM HEAT: Heat applied beneath growing plants by means of hot water, steam or electricity. The expression "Ten degrees of bottom heat" means that the bed should be 10 degrees warmer than the air just above the bed or in the propagating house.

BUDDING OR BUD GRAFTING: Form of grafting in which a single bud with little or no wood is applied to the cambium of the stock.

BULB: Specialized structure of dormancy and reproduction, consisting of a short stem and thick, scale-like fleshy leaf bases. An onion or a lily bulb are true bulbs. A dahlia "bulb" is a tuberous root, not a bulb.

BULBIL: Small bulb-like structure formed on the aerial portion of a stem or inflorescence.

BULBLET: Diminutive bulb formed on the bulb scales or on the underground portions of the stem.

CALLUS: Non-differentiated parenchyma cells. Often the new formation of cells around injured tissue. It appears most conspicuously at the lower end of a stem cutting, the cut surface of a layer or of a root graft, but also at the apical ends of cuttings where cut.

CAMBIUM: Thin layer of tissue capable of meristematic growth located between the phloem (bark) and the xylem (wood).

CHIMERA: Plant or plant part composed of 2 or more genetically distinct tissues growing adjacent to each other, usually caused by mutation.

CLONE: Group of plants propagated asexually from one original individual.

COLDFRAME: Enclosed plot of earth usually covered with glass or plastic but without supplemental heat.

COMPLETE FLOWER: Contains stamens, pistils, petals, and sepals.

COMPOST: Mixed and rotted vegetable matter, particularly manure and litter. (In Britain, a growing medium or mixture.)

CORM: Short, erect, bulblike, fleshy stem, bearing thin or reduced scale-like leaves and usually growing underground, e.g., gladiolus, crocus.

CROSS-POLLINATION: Transfer of pollen from a stamen of one plant to a stigma of another plant; or in the older sense, pollination involving 2 flowers on the same plant or on different plants.

CROWN: Junction of root and stem, in seedlings the hypocotyl region.

CULTIVAR: Cultivated variety: an assemblage of cultivated plants which is clearly distinguished by many characters and which, when reproduced, retains its distinguishing characteristics.

CUTTAGE: Propagation by plant parts (roots, rhizomes, tubers, stems, or leaves) cut in pieces with or without buds. These pieces produce missing parts and asexually produce new plants of the same cultivar and species as the parent plant.

CUTTING: Piece of a plant used in propagation which regenerates missing parts.

CYTOKININ: Natural endogenous hormones that appear to control seed germination.

DAMPING OFF: Disease of plants which causes them to decay, typically caused by fungi such as Rhizoctonia and Pythium.

DICOTYLEDONOUS PLANTS: Subclass of flowering plants characterized by having seeds with two cotyledons, netted-veined leaves and the parts of the flower usually in fours or fives.

DIOECIOUS: Plants bearing flowers of only one sex; e.g., Holly. (Compare with MONOECIOUS).

DIPLOID: (2N) - An organism possessing 2 complete sets of chromosomes in each somatic cell.

DISBUDDING: Removing side buds.

DISTAL: That portion of stem or root furthest from the crown or ground line.

DIVISION: Commonly applied to that phase of separation in which the parts are cut or broken into pieces, in contrast to natural separation.

DORMANCY: A condition of inactivity, e.g., buds or seeds.

EMBRYOID: Embryo-like body developing asexually in tissue culture. A true embryo is formed by the union of sexual gametes.

EVERGREENS: Plants which retain their leaves through the winter.

EXPLANT: Portion of the plant that is placed into tissue culture, i.e., embryos, seeds, stems, leaves, roots or floral parts.

EYES: Buds found on true (stem) tubers, e.g., Irish potato.

FLAT: Shallow box in which seeds are started and seedlings grown. Usually of some standard size that fits the requirements of the propagator. It is also used as a tray for carrying potted plants.

GERMINATION: Resumption of active growth by the embryo and the development of a young plant from a seed.

GRAFTING: General term for vegetative propagation of plants on roots other than their own.

GROWTH REGULATOR: Synthetic compounds or plant hormones that modify plant physiological processes.

HAPLOID: (1N) Possessing one-half the normal complement of chromosomes.

HARDENING-OFF: Process of acclimating young plants grown in the greenhouse to outside conditions.

HARDY: Term applied to those plants which resist stress, e.g., in cold hardiness those annuals which resist frost in the fall and to those perennial plants which may be left outdoors all winter.

HEAVING: Lifting of plants out of the soil by the alternate freezing and thawing of the soil.

HEEL CUTTING: Cutting which retains a portion of the parent branch at its base. Often the part retained when the bark adheres to the base of a cutting torn or cut from the parent branch (compare with MALLET CUTTING).

HEELING-IN: Temporary placing of plants on an angle in a shallow trench and covering the roots with soil and watering well.

HERB: Plant whose aerial parts die at the end of the growing season.

HERBACEOUS: Not woody, dying down each year. Also said of soft branches before they become woody.

HORMONE: Organic compounds other than nutrients produced by plants which in low concentrations regulate plant physiological processes.

HOTBED: Enclosed plot of earth usually covered with glass and provided with some means of supplemental heat (steam, hot water pipes or electric current).

HYBRID: Result of a cross between two plants which are more or less unlike, e.g., two inbreds or clones.

IMBIBITION: Physical absorption of water by a seed prior to and in preparation for germination.

IMPERFECT FLOWER: Flower with one set of sexual organs (stamen or pistil) missing.

INARCHING: Placing two plants together in such a way that they will graft and grow together while still growing on their own roots.

INHIBITOR: Any substance which slows or causes the cessation of a process.

INTERSTOCK: A stem piece inserted between a stock (rootstock) and scion in the operation called "Doubleworking".

IN VITRO: Culture of tissue outside the living organism.

IN VIVO: Occurring within the organism.

JUVENILE: An immature form of a plant incapable of fruiting. Leaf and habit may differ from mature form.

LAMINATE BULBS: Bulbs made up of more or less continuous and close-fitting layers or plates, as in the onion. (Tunicate bulbs are laminate.)

LATERAL BUDS: Buds that are situated on the sides of branches, usually in leaf axils.

LAYERING: Method of vegetative propagation in which a portion of a plant is induced to form roots while still attached to the parent plant.

LEAF MOLD: Decomposition product of leaves, as in a soil mixture for acid-loving plants.

LIFE CYCLE: History of a plant from germination through vegetation, flowering, fruiting and death. Life cycles vary in duration from a few days
to weeks to many centuries.

MALLET CUTTING: A cutting which retains a section of 2 year wood at its
base. (Compare with HEEL CUTTING).

MEDIUM (PLURAL - MEDIA): Supporting substance, water, soil or mixtures of
sand, peat, perlite, etc., on or in which plants are grown or cultured.

MICROPROPAGATION: Development of new plants in an artificial medium under
aseptic conditions from small pieces of plants.

MIST: A fine water spray automatically controlled. Sprayed on the leaves
of cuttings to prevent wilting.

MONOCOTYLEDONOUS PLANTS: Subclass of flowering plants. The stems have no
annual layers, the parts of the flowers are usually in threes (never in
fives) and the leaves parallel veined. (Grasses are monocotyldeonous
plants.)

MONOECIOUS: Separate male and female flowers, on the same plant (compare with
DIOECIOUS).

MULCH: A covering over the soil for protection against drying-out, winter
injury, weeds, etc.

MUTATION: A sudden change in genetic composition of a cell, tissue, organ or
complete plant.

NODE: Portion of a stem to which a leaf is attached.

OFFSETS: Short, lateral branches or stolons produced near the bases of
plants to serve in natural propagation. They usually take root and
become new plants.

PEAT: Semi-decayed organic matter produced by the deposit of successive
generations of plants growing in standing water.

PERENNIAL: A plant which lives for more than 2 years.

PERLITE: A medium made from heat-expanded volcanic rock, generally inert
and added to improve drainage of a soil mix.

PETIOLE: Leaf stalk.

pH: Generally accepted symbolical means of specifying the degree of free
acidity or free alkalinity of soils.

PINCH: To remove the terminal portion of a plant thereby causing branching.

POLARITY: Development of roots and shoots on the ends of cuttings which is
correlated with their orientation on the parent plant (see DISTAL and
PROXIMAL).

POLLINATION: Transfer of pollen from the anther to the stigma of the same or another flower.

POLYEMBRYONY: Presence of more than 1 embryo in a seed.

POT-BOUND: Phrase referring to those plants which have remained too long in the same pots and have been stunted in growth.

PROPAGATION: Multiplication or increase in number of plants or animals in the perpetuation of the species.

PROXIMAL: That portion of stem or root tissue nearest the crown or ground line.

PSEUDOBULB: A specialized storage structure produced in many orchid species consisting of an enlarged, fleshy section of stem tissues with 1 or more nodes.

RAFFIA: Lower epidermis of a Madagascar palm (Raffia ruffia) peeled in narrow strips and used in tying vines, flowers and in graftage.

RHIZOMES: Horizontal underground stem, often root-like in appearance, e.g., German Iris.

ROOTSTOCK: See STOCK.

RUNNER: Modified stem which develops from a leaf axil in the crown of a plant, extends horizontally on the surface of the soil and takes root at one or more of the nodes.

SCALY BULBS: Bulbs composed of narrow, loose overlapping fleshy leaf bases and lacking a protective tunic.

SCARIFICATION: Mechanical means of modifying hard or impervious seed coats.

SCION (CION): Any plant part, usually of a stem, inserted in a stock for propagation.

SEED: Mature ovule, consisting of an embryonic plant, usually containing stored food and enclosed by one or 2 seed coats.

SHIFTING: Transferring of potted plants to larger-sized pots.

SEPARATION: Multiplication of plants by means of naturally detachable vegetative organs. It is effected by means of bulbs, scales, corms, tubers, etc.

STERILIZING (PASTEURIZATION): Practice used to destroy existing undesirable organisms in the soil by the use of steam, boiling water or chemicals.

SPORT: Plant or plant-part, which unexpectedly shows a character different from that of the cultivar or species.

SPHAGNUM: Large group of generally bog mosses widely used for packaging plants. Also used as a growing medium.

STOCK (ROOTSTOCK, UNDERSTOCK): In a grafting or budding operation that part of the plant which is to receive the bud or the scion.

STOLON: Horizontal stem just above or beneath the soil, which roots at the end or at the nodes.

STRATIFICATION: Treatment of dormant seeds with high or low temperatures to bring about prompt, uniform germination by overcoming a physiological dormancy.

SUBERIZATION: Process by which a cut surface of a stem or root forms a protective resinous or corky layer, especially under conditions of high temperatures and humidity.

SUBIRRIGATION: Various automatic methods of supplying water from the bottom of the bed without wetting plant foliage.

SUCKER: Shoot which arises from an adventitious bud on a root.

TISSUE CULTURE: Culture of isolated tissues in an aseptic condition.

TOPWORKING: Grafting of an established plant to change the cultivar.

TOTIPOTENCY: Possession of the total genetic complement by all living cells of the organism and theoretically each cell is therefore capable of regenerating an entire plant identical to the parent.

TUBER: Modified stem which develops underground and has nodes with leaf scars and buds, and internodes.

TUBEROUS ROOTS: Fleshy underground structures lacking nodes and internodes, true root tissues.

TUNICATE BULB: Nonscaly bulbs characterized by fleshy leaf bases arranged in concentric layers around a central growing point, with a dry outer membranous tunic.

UNDERSTOCK: See STOCK.

VERMICULITE: Material made from heat expanded mica ore and used as a medium for plant propagation and culture.

WARDIAN CASE: Transparent container tightly fitted with an adjustable glass cover in which plants are grown or cuttings rooted.

WATER SPROUT: A shoot arising from a latent bud on a stem.

APPENDIX II – ROOTING SELECTED WOODY ORNAMENTALS

SPECIES	COMMON NAME	TYPE CUTTING	TIME OF YEAR	TREATMENT
Abelia grandiflora	Abelia	Softwood	July-August	IBA 12.5 ppm/24 hrs
Abies concolor	White Fir	Hardwood	December	IBA 100 ppm/20 hrs
		Hardwood	January	No treatment
		Hardwood	January	Hormodin 3
Abies frazeri	Fraser Fir	Hardwood	January	IBA 200 ppm/24 hrs
Abies veitchii	Veitch Fir	Hardwood	Dec-Jan	Hormodin 3
Acer palmatum	Japanese Maple	Softwood (T)	Early summer	IBA 2% Powder
Acer rubrum	Red Maple	Softwood	June	IBA 200 ppm/6 hrs
Acer saccharum	Sugar Maple	Softwood	June	Hormodin 1
Albizzia julibrissin	Mimosa	Softwood	June	No treatment
Amelanchier canadensis	Shadbush	Softwood	Summer	IBA 50 ppm/24 hrs
		Hardwood	April	
Aralia chinensis	Aralia	Root cuttings	December	No treatment
Arctostaphylos Uva-ursi	Bearberry	Terminal cuttings	October	No treatment
				IBA 3 mg/gm Talc
Aronia arbutifolia	Chokeberry	Softwood	Summer	None
Berberis julianae	Juliana Barberry	Softwood	July	None
Berberis thunbergii	Japanese Barberry	Softwood	August	None
Betula pendula	European Birch	Softwood	August	IAA 50 ppm/32 hrs
Betula papyrifera	Canoe Birch	Softwood	August	IBA 20 ppm/24 hrs
Betula populifolia	Gray Birch	Softwood	July	IBA 50 ppm/6 hrs
Buddleia davidii	Butterflybush	Softwood	June-July	IBA 33 ppm/24 hrs
			June-July	None
Buxus sempervirens	Boxwood	Softwood	Summer	Untreated
Calluna vulgaris	Heather	Soft-wood	Summer, Fall or Winter	Untreated
			December	IBA 40 ppm/24 hrs
Calycanthus floridus	Allspice	Softwood	July	Hormodin 2
Camellia japonica	Camellia	Hardwood	July	IBA 100 ppm/24 hrs
Carya illinoensis	Pecan	Hardwood	March	IBA 100 ppm/24 hrs
Castanea mollissima	Chinese Chestnut	Softwood	June	Hormodin 2
Catalpa sp.	Catalpa	Root cuttings	December	
Cedrus libani	Cedar of Lebanon	Hardwood	Fall	Untreated
Cephalotaxus drupacea	Japanese Plum Yew	Hardwood	November	IBA 60 ppm/24 hrs

291

SPECIES	COMMON NAME	TYPE CUTTING	TIME OF YEAR	TREATMENT
Cercis canadensis	Redbud	Softwood	June-July	Untreated
Chaenomeles lagenaria	Japanese Quince	Softwood	Summer	IBA 12.5 ppm/24 hrs
		Softwood	June	Hormodin 2
Chamaecyparis lawsoniana	Lawson Cypress	Hardwood	Fall	Untreated
Chamaecyparis obtusa	Hinoki Cypress	Hardwood	Sept-Jan	Hormodin 3
Chamaecyparis pisifera	Sawara Cypress	Hardwood	Nov-Dec	IBA 75 ppm/24 hrs
Chionanthus sp.	Fringe Tree	Softwood	June	IBA 1:250 Talc
Cladrastis lutea	Yellowwood	Root cuttings	December	
Clematis sp.	Clematis	Softwood	Summer	
Clethra alnifolia	Sweet Pepperbush	Softwood	Summer	IBA 10 ppm/24 hrs
Comptonia peregrina	Sweet Fern	Root cuttings	December	
Cornus alba	Siberian Dogwood	Softwood	June	IBA 50 ppm/24 hrs
Cornus amomum	Silky Dogwood	Softwood	July	
Cornus florida	Flowering Dogwood	Softwood	June	IBA 12.5 ppm/24 hrs
Cornus kousa	Japanese Dogwood	Softwood	July	IBA 25 ppm/24 hrs
Cornus mas	Cornelian Cherry	Softwood	July	IBA 25 ppm/20 hrs
Cornus racemosa	Gray Dogwood	Softwood	June	IBA 25 ppm/20 hrs
		Softwood	June	IBA 30 ppm/12 hrs
Cornus stolonifera	Red-Osier Dogwood	Softwood	August	Untreated
Corylus avellana	European Hazel	Softwood	Summer	IBA 100 ppm/24 hrs
Corylus maxima	Filbert	Softwood	July	Hormodin 2
Cotinus coggygria	Smoketree	Softwood	June	IBA 50 ppm/24 hrs
Cotoneaster apiculata	Cranberry Cotoneaster	Softwood	Early summer	Untreated
Cotoneaster divaricata	Spreading Cotoneaster	Softwood	July	Untreated
Cotoneaster horizontalis	Rock Spray Cotoneaster	Softwood	Mid-June	Untreated
		Hardwood	December	Untreated
Cotoneaster microphylla	Small-leaved Cotoneaster	Softwood	September	Untreated
Cryptomeria japonica	Cryptomeria	Softwood	Summer	IBA 40-80 ppm/24 hrs
		Hardwood	December	IBA 12 mg/gm Talc
Cydonia oblonga	Quince	Softwood	Spring	IBA 20 ppm/24 hrs
Cytisus scoparis	Scotch Broom	Softwood	June	IBA 50 ppm/24 hrs
Daphne cneorum	Rose Daphne	Softwood	Summer	Hormodin 2
		Hardwood	December	IBA 50 ppm/24 hrs

SPECIES	COMMON NAME	TYPE CUTTING	TIME OF YEAR	TREATMENT
Daphne mezerem	February Daphne	Root cuttings	December	IBA 100 ppm/24 hrs
Davidia involucrata	Dove Tree	Hardwood	January	Hormodin 2
		Softwood	September	Untreated
Deutzia gracilis	Slender Deutzia	Softwood	July	Untreated
Elaeagnus angustifolia	Russian Olive	Hardwood	October	IBA 40 ppm/24 hrs
Elaeagnus pungens	Thorny Eleagnus	Hardwood	October	IBA 30 ppm/24 hrs
Enkianthus campanulatus	Redvein Enkianthus	Softwood	May-June	IBA 50 ppm/20 hrs
Erica sp.	Heath	Softwood	June	Untreated
Euonymus alata	Winged Euonymus	Softwood	April-May	Untreated
Euonymus fortunei	Wintercreeper	Softwood		
Euonymus fortunei cv. coloratus		Softwood	August	Untreated or Hormodin 2
" cv. minima		Softwood	August	Untreated or Hormodin 2
Exchorda racemosa	Pearlbush	Softwood	June-July	IBA 50 ppm/24 hrs
Fagus sylvatica	European Beech	Softwood	June-July	IAA 50 ppm/24 hrs
Forsythia sp.	Forsythia	Softwood	May-Sept	Untreated or Hormodin 2
		Hardwood	Nov-Feb	Untreated
Franklinia alatamaha	Franklinia	Softwood	Late summer	IBA 30 ppm/24 hrs
Gardenia sp.	Gardenia	Softwood	Sept-Oct	Hormodin 3 & Phygon XL
		Softwood		With or without Hormodin 2
Ginkgo biloba	Ginkgo	Softwood	June	IBA 50 ppm/24 hrs or Hormodin 3
Gleditsia triacanthos	Honeylocust	Root cuttings	April	(If trees are on own roots.)
		Hardwood	Dec-Jan	IBA 300 ppm/72 hrs
		Softwood		Only if taken from young trees.
Gymnocladus dioicus	Kentucky Coffeetree	Root cuttings	December	Untreated
Halesia carolina	Silverbells	Softwood	July	IBA 25 ppm/20 hrs
Hamamelis mollis	Witch-hazels	Softwood	July	IBA 50 ppm/20 hrs
Hedera helix	Ivy	Softwood	July	
Hydrangea quercifolia	Oakleaf Hydrangea	Softwood	Summer	Hormodin 2
Ilex cornuta burfordi	Burford Holly	Evergreen-Hardwood	Summer	IBA 30-80 ppm/24 hrs
		Root cuttings	Autumn	

SPECIES	COMMON NAME	TYPE CUTTING	TIME OF YEAR	TREATMENT
Ilex crenata	Japanese Holly	Evergreen-Hardwood	Autumn	Untreated
Ilex glabra	Inkberry	Softwood	July-August	Untreated
Ilex opaca	American Holly	Hardwood	Later summer	IBA 50 ppm/24 hrs
Juniperus sp.	Juniper	Hardwood	Nov-Feb	Hormodin 2 or 3
Kalmia latifolia	Mt. Laurel	Softwood	August	Hormodin 3
Kerria japonica	Kerria	Softwood	Summer	Untreated
Koelreuteria paniculata	Koelreuteria	Root cuttings	December	
Laburnum watereri	Laburnum	Leaf bud cuttings	Summer	
Leucothoe catesbaei	Leucothoe	Softwood	July	IBA 10 ppm/24 hrs
Ligustrum sp.	Privet	Softwood	Summer	Hormodin 1 or 2
Magnolia soulangeana	Saucer Magnolia	Softwood	June	IBA 50 ppm/24 hrs
Mahonia aquifolia	Oregon Grape Holly	Softwood	July-August	Untreated
Malus sp.	Apple	Softwood	Late spring	Hormodin 3
			Early summer	
Osmanthus ilicifolius	Osmanthus	Softwood	Summer	Untreated
Oxydendron arboreum	Sorrel-Tree	Softwood	July	IBA 90 ppm/8 hrs
Pachysandra terminalis	Pachysandra	Softwood	Summer	IBA 30 ppm/6 hrs
Philadelphus sp.	Philadelphus	Softwood	Spring	Hormodin 3
Photinia serrulata	Photinia	Softwood	Summer	IBA 20 ppm/6 hrs
Picea abies	Norway Spruce	Evergreen-Hardwood	Nov-Feb	Untreated
Picea glauca	White Spruce	Softwood	July	Untreated
Picea mariana	Black Spruce	Evergreen-Hardwood	December	Untreated
Picea omorika	Serbian Spruce	Evergreen-Hardwood	Winter	IBA 200 ppm/24 hrs
Picea pungens	Colorado Spruce	Evergreen-Hardwood	February	IBA 100 ppm/24 hrs
Pieris japonica	Japanese Pieris	Softwood	July-August	IBA 10 ppm/24 hrs
		Hardwood	January	Hormodin 2
Pinus strobus	Eastern White Pine	Hardwood	March	IBA 200 ppm/5 hrs
Poncirus trifoliata	Poncirus	Softwood	July	IBA 50 ppm/24 hrs
Populus alba	White Poplar	Hardwood	December	IBA 50 ppm/30 hrs
		Softwood	July-August	IBA 50 ppm/24 hrs
Potentilla fruticosa	Cinquefoil	Softwood	June-July	Hormodin 2
Prunus cerasifera	Flowering Almond	Softwood	July	NAA 30 ppm/12 hrs
Prunus glandulosa		Softwood	July	Untreated
Prunus laurocerasus	Cherry Laurel	Softwood	Summer	IBA 40 ppm/6 hrs
Prunus persica	Peach	Softwood	Summer	IBA 2000 ppm/1 min

294

SPECIES	COMMON NAME	TYPE CUTTING	TIME OF YEAR	TREATMENT
Prunus subhirtella	Higan Cherry	Softwood	July	IBA 25 ppm/20 hrs
Pseudotsuga menziesii	Douglas Fir	Hardwood	Winter	IBA 50 ppm/24 hrs
Pyracantha coccinea	Pyracantha	Softwood	Summer	Untreated
Pyrus communis	Pear	Softwood	Summer	NAA 40 ppm/12 hrs
Quercus sp.	Oak	In general propagation of oaks remains for research-er - not grower. Try cuttings from trees less than 6 years old and use growth regulator treatments and vary time of taking the cuttings. Very difficult. Response varies with time of year, growth regulator, age of tree, etc.		
Rhododendron catawbiense	Rhododendron	(Leaf bud or terminal)	September	Hormodin 3 + Ferbam 3:1
Rhododendron obtusum	Azalea	Softwood	July	Hormodin 2
Rhodotypos scandens	Jetbead	Softwood	Spring	IBA 25 ppm/24 hrs
Ribes alpinum	Alpine Currant	Hardwood	Winter	
		Softwood	July	IBA 20 ppm/24 hrs
Robinia pseudoacacia	Robinia	Root cuttings	December	
Rosa sp.	Rose	Softwood	All year	Hormodin 1
Rubus sp.	Raspberry	(Leaf Bud) Softwood	May-July	
Sassafras albidum	Sassafras	Root cuttings	December	
Sciadopitys verticillata	Umbrella Pine	Evergreen-Hardwood	January	NAA 100 ppm/24 hrs
Spirea sp.	Spirea	Softwood	Summer	Hormodin 1 or 2
Stewartia koreana	Stewartia	Softwood	June	Hormodin 3
Symphoricarpos orbiculatus	Coralberry	Softwood	June-August	IBA 5 ppm/24 hrs
Syringa vulgaris	Lilac	Softwood	May-June	IBA 20-60 ppm/24 hrs
Taxus cuspidata	Japanese Yew	Evergreen-Hardwood	Oct-Jan	Hormodin 3
Thuja occidentalis	Arborvitae	Heel cuttings	Nov-March	Hormodin 2
Tsuga canadensis	Canadian Hemlock	Evergreen-Hardwood	August-April	Hormodin 3
Ulmus japonica	Japanese Elm	Softwood	June	Hormodin 2
Viburnum sp.	Viburnum	Softwood	Summer	Hormodin 2
Weigela florida	Weigela	Softwood	June	IBA 50 ppm/12 hrs
Wisteria floribunda	Japanese Wisteria	Softwood	July	IBA 25 ppm/24 hrs

APPENDIX III — PROPAGATING SELECTED HOUSE PLANTS

GENUS	COMMON NAME	SOFTWOOD CUTTINGS	HARDWOOD CUTTINGS	ROOT CUTTINGS	DIVISION	LAYERING	GRAFTING	BUDDING	OFFSETS	SEEDS	NOTES
Abutilon	Flowering Maple	X								X	
Acacia	Mimosa	X		X						X	Soak seeds overnight.
Achimenes	Achimenes	X			X						
Acorus	Japanese Sweet Flag				X						
Adiantum	Maidenhair Fern				X					X	Spores
Aechmea	Bromeliad									X	Remove and root suckers.
Agapanthus	African Lily				X						
Agave	Century Plant	X								X	Remove and root suckers.
Aglaonema	Chinese Evergreen	X			X						
Aloe	Aloe	X								X	Remove and root suckers.
Alternanthera	Joseph's Coat	X				X					
Anthurium	Anthurium				X					X	
Aphelandra	Aphelandra, Zebra Plant	X								X	
Araucaria	Norfolk Island Pine									X	
Aspidistra	Cast Iron Plant				X						
Asplenium nidus	Birds Nest Fern				X						
Begonia	Begonia	X								X	
Beloperone	Shrimp Plant	X			X						
Billbergia	Bromeliad	X			X					X	
Bougainvillea	Bougainvillea	X									
Brassaia	Schefflera					X				X	
Bryophyllum	Mother-of-Thousands	X									Foliar embryos, remove and plant.
Caladium	Caladium				X					X	
Calathea	Calathea	X			X						
Calceolaria	Calceolaria				X					X	
Campanula	Bellflower				X					X	
Capsicum	Ornamental Pepper				X					X	
Carex	Sedge				X					X	
Carissa	Natal Plum	X									
Ceropegia	Rosary Plant				X						
Chamaedorea	Palm				X					X	

297

GENUS	COMMON NAME	SOFTWOOD CUTTINGS	HARDWOOD CUTTINGS	ROOT CUTTINGS	DIVISION	LAYERING	GRAFTING	BUDDING	OFFSETS	SEEDS	NOTES
Chlorophytum	Spider Plant	X			X						
Chrysanthemum	Mum	X			X					X	
Cissus	Treebine, Grape Ivy	X									
Citrus	Lemon	X					X	X		X	
Clivia	Kafir Lily				X						
Codiaeum	Croton	X									
Coleus	Coleus	X									
Columnea	Columnea	X									
Cordyline	Ti Plant	X			X					X	
Crassula	Jade Plant	X									
Cryptanthus	Cryptanthus	X									
Cyclamen	Cyclamen									X	
Davallia	Hare's Foot Fern				X						Spores.
Dieffenbachia	Dumb Cane	X									
Dizygotheca	Threadleaf, False Aralia	X									
Dracaena	Dracaena	X				X					
Echeveria	Echeveria	X							X	X	
Episcia	Episcia	X							X	X	
Euphorbia	Poinsettia	X									
Fatshedera	Fatshedera	X	X								
Fatsia	Fatsia	X				X					
Ficus benjamina	Java Fig	X				X					
Ficus elastica	Rubber Plant	X				X					
Ficus lyrata	Fiddle Leaf Fig	X				X					
Fortunella	Kumquat						X	X			
Fuchsia	Fuchsia	X								X	
Gynura	Velvet Plant	X								X	
Hedera	Ivy	X				X	X			X	
Hibiscus	Hibiscus	X	X			X	X			X	
Hippeastrum	Amaryllis								X	X	
Hoya	Wax Plant	X									
Hyacinthus	Hyacinth									X	Score bulbs.
Hydrangea	Hydrangea	X	X		X					X	
Impatiens	Impatiens	X			X					X	

GENUS	COMMON NAME	SOFTWOOD CUTTINGS	HARDWOOD CUTTINGS	ROOT CUTTINGS	DIVISION	LAYERING	GRAFTING	BUDDING	OFFSETS	SEEDS	NOTES
Iresine	Bloodleaf	X									
Jasminum	Jasmine	X	X			X				X	
Kalanchoe	Kalanchoe, Air Plant	X								X	Remove and plant foliar embryos.
Kalanchoe tomentosa	Panda Plant	X									
Lantana	Lantana	X								X	
Lilium	Lily				X				X	X	Bulbils on stems. Scale bulbs.
Maranta	Prayer Plant	X			X					X	
Monstera	Split Leaf Philodendron	X									
Nephrolepsis	Boston Fern				X						
Nerium	Oleander	X									
Oxalis	Oxalis				X					X	
Pandanus	Screw Pine	X									
Passiflora	Passion Flower	X								X	
Pelargonium	Geranium	X									
Pellaea	Cliff Brake				X					X	Spores.
Peperomia	Peperomia	X									
Persea	Avocado	X								X	
Philodendron	Philodendron	X				X				X	
Pilea cadierii	Aluminum Plant	X									
Pilea microphyla	Artillery Plant	X									
Pittosporum	Pittosporum	X									
Platycerium	Staghorn Fern				X					X	Spores.
Plectranthus	Swedish Ivy	X								X	
Podocarpus	Yew	X									
Polypodium	Resurrection Fern				X					X	Spores.
Polyscias	Polyscias		X	X	X		X				
Pteris	Table Fern		X		X					X	
Punica	Pomegranate		X			X	X	X		X	
Saintpaulia	African Violet	X			X	X					Divide multi-crowned plants.
Sagittaria	Arrowhead				X					X	
Sansevieria	Snake Plant	X		X	X						

GENUS	COMMON NAME	SOFTWOOD CUTTINGS	HARDWOOD CUTTINGS	ROOT CUTTINGS	DIVISION	LAYERING	GRAFTING	BUDDING	OFFSETS	SEEDS	NOTES
Saxifraga	Strawberry Geranium				X					X	
Scindapsus	Pothos	X		X							
Sedum	Stone Crop	X			X					X	
Senecio	Cineraria	X		X	X					X	
Senecio	German Ivy	X									
Sinningia	Gloxinia	X								X	
Solanum	Jerusalem Cherry	X								X	
Strelitzia	Bird of Paradise				X					X	
Streptocarpus	Cape Primrose	X			X					X	
Tolmiea	Piggyback Plant	X									Foliar embryos.
Tradescantia	Wandering Jew	X			X						
Vinca	Periwinkle	X			X	X				X	
Zantedeschia	Calla								X	X	
Zebrina	Wandering Jew	X									

APPENDIX IV — WOODY PLANTS AND HERBACEOUS PERENNIAL GENERA THAT ARE CAPABLE OF BEING PROPAGATED BY ROOT CUTTINGS

WOODY PLANTS

Aesculus
Ailanthus
Albizia
Alnus
Amelanchier
Aralia
Ardesia
Aronia
Berberis
Calycanthus
Camellia
Campsis
Caragana
Catalpa
Ceonanthus
Cladrastis
Clerodendron
Cydonia
Daphne
Eleagnus
Forthergilla
Gymnocladus
Halesia
Hypericum
Koelreuteria
Lagerstroemia

Ligustrum
Lonicera
Maclura
Malus
Morus
Myrica
Paulownia
Prunus
Pyrus
Rhus
Robinia
Rosa
Rubus
Sambucus
Sassafras
Sophora
Syringa
Tamarix
Tilia
Ulmus
Viburnum
Wisteria
Weigela
Xanthocerus
Yucca
Zanthoxylum

HERBACEOUS PERENNIALS

Achillea
Anchusa
Anemone
Asclepias
Campanula
Ceratostigma
Clematis
Convolvulus
Dicentra
Dictamnus
Dodocatheon
Echinops
Euphorbia
Gypsophila
Gaillardia
Helianthus

Ipomea
Limonium
Monarda
Oenothera
Paeonia
Papaver
Phlox
Polygonatum
Salvia
Saponaria
Senecio
Stokesia
Thermopsis
Trollius
Verbascum

301

APPENDIX V — LAYERING SELECTED WOODY ORNAMENTALS

SPECIES	COMMON NAME	TYPE OF LAYERAGE	TIME PERFORMED
Berberis sp.	Barberry	Simple,Mound	Spring
Betula sp.	Birch	Simple	Spring,Summer
Buxus sp.	Boxwood	Simple	Summer
Camellia sp.	Camellia	Simple	Spring
Chaenomeles sp.	Flowering Quince	Mound	Spring
Clematis sp.	Clematis	Simple,Compound	Spring,Summer
Cotoneaster sp.	Cotoneaster	Simple,Compound	Summer
Cornus sp.	Dogwood	Simple,Continuous	Spring,Summer
Corylus sp.	Filbert	Simple	Summer
Dieffenbachia sp.	Dumbcane	Air	Anytime
Dracaena sp.	Dracaena	Air	Anytime
Euonymus sp.	Euonymus	Simple	Spring
Fatshedera lizei	Tree Ivy	Air	Anytime
Ficus benjamina	Weeping Fig	Air	Anytime
Ficus elastica decora	Rubber Plant	Air	Anytime
Ficus lyrata	Fiddle-leaf Fig	Air	Anytime
Forsythia sp.	Forsythia	Tip,Simple	Summer
Hedera helix	Ivy	Simple	Spring
Hydrangea sp.	Hydrangea	Simple	Spring
Ilex sp.	Holly	Air,Simple	Summer,Fall
Jasminium sp.	Jasmine	Simple	Spring
Juniperus sp.	Juniper	Simple	Summer
Kalmia latifolia	Mountain Laurel	Simple	Summer
Lonicera sp.	Honeysuckle	Simple	Spring,Summer
Magnolia sp.	Magnolia	Mound	Spring
Malus sp.	Apple	Mound,Trench	Spring
Monstera deliciosa	Split leaf Philodendron	Air,Simple	Anytime
Nerium oleander	Oleander	Simple	Spring,Summer
Parthenocissus quinquefolia	Virginia Creeper	Compound	Summer
Philodendron sp.	Philodendron	Simple,Compound,Air	Anytime
Pittosporum tobira	Pittosporum	Air	Anytime
Rhamnus sp.	Buckthorn	Simple	Spring
Rhododendron sp.	Rhododendron	Simple,Trench	Summer,Spring
Ribes sp.	Currant	Mound	Spring
Rosa sp.	Rose	Simple,Tip	Spring,Summer
Rubus sp.	Raspberry,black,purple	Tip	Summer
Salix sp.	Willow	Simple	Spring
Syringa vulgaris	Lilac	Air	Spring
Tilia americana	Linden	Simple,Mound (of suckers)	Spring
Tsuga sp.	Hemlock	Simple	Spring
Vaccinium sp.	Blueberry	Mound	Spring
Viburnum sp.	Viburnum	Simple	Spring,Summer

SPECIES	COMMON NAME	TYPE OF LAYERAGE	TIME PERFORMED
Vitis sp.	Grape	Simple,Compound	Spring
Weigela sp.	Weigela	Simple	Spring
Wisteria sp.	Wisteria	Simple	Spring

APPENDIX VI – GUIDELINES FOR THE GERMINATION OF SOME ANNUAL, POT PLANT AND ORNAMENTAL HERB SEEDS

SPECIES	COMMON NAME	Group[1]	Approximate number seeds per oz	Optimum temperature for best germination (°C)	Continuous light or dark[2]	Usual time required for uniform germination (days)
Ageratum houstonianum	Ageratum	VI	200,000	21	L	5
Allium schoenoprasum	Chives	IV	22,000	16	DL	10
Althaea rosea	Hollyhock	IV	2,000	16	DL	10
Amaranthus tricolor	Amaranthus	III	47,000	21	DL	10
Anethum graveolens	Dill	IV	6,300	16	L	10
Antirrhinum majus	Snapdragon	VII	180,000	18	L	10
Asparagus asparagoides	Smilax	VIII	4,000	24	D	30
Begonia semperflorens	Begonia, Fibrous-rooted	V	2,000,000	21	L	15
Begonia x tuberhybrida	Begonia, Tuberous-rooted	VI	2,000,000	18	L	15
Borago officinalis	Borage	VIII	2,100	21	D	8
Browallia speciosa	Browallia	VI	130,000	21	L	15
Browallia viscosa Compacta	Browallia	V	340,000	21	L	15
Calceolaria x herbeohybrida	Calceolaria	VI	600,000	21	L	15
Calendula officinalis	Calendula	VIII	3,000	21	D	10
Callistephus chinensis	Aster	I	12,000	21	DL	8
Campanula medium	Campanula	III	50,000	21	DL	20
Celosia argentea	Celosia	III	28,000	21	DL	10
Centaurea cyanus	Centaurea	VIII	7,000	18	D	10
Centaurea gymnocarpa	Centaurea	VIII	7,000	18	D	10
Centaurea moschata	Centaurea	VIII	7,000	21	D	10
Cheiranthus cheiri	Wallflower	I	14,000	21	DL	5
Clarkia elegans	Clarkia	I	90,000	21	DL	5
Cobaea scandens	Cobaea	I	375	21	DL	15
Coleus blumei	Coleus	VII	100,000	18	L	10
Convolvulus sp.	Morning Glory	III	650	18	DL	5
Coriandrum sativum	Coriander	VIII	1,240	21	D	10
Cosmos bipinnatus	Cosmos	II	5,000	21	DL	5
Cuphea Llavea var. miniata	Cuphea	VI	7,000	21	L	8
Cyclamen persicum	Cyclamen	IX	2,500	16	D	50
Cynoglossum amabile	Cynoglossum	IV	5,000	16	D	5

SPECIES	COMMON NAME	Group[1]	Approximate number seeds per oz	Optimum temperature for best germination (°C)	Continuous light or dark[2]	Usual time required for uniform germination (days)
Dahlia pinnata	Dahlia	I	2,800	21	DL	5
Delphinium ajacis	Larkspur	IX	8,000	13	D	20
Dianthus caryophyllus	Carnation	IV	14,000	21	DL	20
Dianthus chinensis	Dianthus	I	25,000	21	DL	5
Dimorphotheca sinuata	Dimorphotheca	II	9,500	21	DL	10
Dorotheanthus bellidiformis	Mesembryanthemum criniflorum	IX	100,000	18	D	15
Euphorbia heterophylla	Euphorbia	I	5,000	21	DL	15
Exacum affine	Exacum	V	1,000,000	21	L	15
Foeniculum vulgare	Fennel	IV	4,000	18	D	10
Freesia (garden cultivars)	Freesia	IV	3,000	18	DL	25
Gaillardia pulchella var. picta	Gaillardia	III	14,000	21	DL	20
Gazania rigens	Gazania	IV	12,000	16	D	8
Gomphrena globosa	Gomphrena	III	5,000	18	D	15
Grevillea robusta	Grevillea	VI	3,000	27	L	20
Gypsophila elegans	Gypsophila	I	2,400	21	DL	10
Helichrysum bracteatum	Helichrysum	VII	36,000	21	L	5
Hunnemannia fumariaefolia	Hunnemannia	III	8,000	21	DL	15
Iberis amara	Candytuft	I	9,600	21	DL	8
Impatiens balsamina	Balsam	III	3,300	21	DL	8
Impatiens holstii	Impatiens	VI	44,000	21	L	15
Kalanchoe blossfeldiana	Kalanchoe	V	2,500,000	21	L	10
Kochia scoparia	Kochia	I	45,000	21	DL	15
Lathyrus odoratus	Sweet pea	IV	350	13	D	15
Limonium sinuatum	Statice	I	350	21	DL	15
Limonium suworowii	Statice	VIII	12,500	21	D	15
Lobelia erinus var. compacta	Lobelia	III	700,000	21	DL	20
Lobularia maritima	Alyssum	I	90,000	21	DL	5
Lonas annua	Ageratum	I	128,000	21	D	5
Lupinus hartwegii	Lupine	IV	1,300	13	DL	20
Majorana hortensis	Marjoram	II	100,000	21	DL	8
Matricaria capensi	Feverfew	VII	145,000	21	L	15
Matthiola incana	Stock	I	16,000	21	DL	10
Mimosa pudica	Mimosa	VIII	4,500	27	D	8

SPECIES	COMMON NAME	Group[1]	Approximate number seeds per oz	Optimum temperature for best germination (°C)	Continuous light or dark[2]	Usual time required for uniform germination (days)
Myosotis sylvatica	Myosotis	IV	44,000	13	D	8
Nemesia strumosa var. suttonii	Nemesia	IX	90,000	18	D	5
Nicotiana alata var. grandiflora	Nicotiana	VII	400,000	21	L	20
Nierembergia hippomanica	Nierembergia	III	175,000	21	DL	15
Ocimum basilicum	Basil	III	9,600	21	DL	10
Ocimum minimum	Basil	III	20,000	21	DL	10
Papaver nudicaule	Iceland Poppy	I	275,000	21	D	10
Penstemon x gloxinioides	Penstemon	VIII	55,000	18	D	10
Perilla frutescens var. crispa	Perilla	VI	20,000	18	L	15
Petroselinum hortense	Parsley	IX	18,500	24	D	15
Petunia hybrida	Petunia	VI	200,000	21	L	10
Phlox drummondii	Phlox	VIII	14,000	18	D	10
Pimpinella anisum	Anise	IV	8,600	21	DL	10
Plumbago capensis	Plumbago	IV	2,000	24	DL	25
Portulaca grandiflora	Portulaca	IV	280,000	21	D	10
Primula malacoides	Primula	VI	385,000	21	L	25
Primula obconica	Primula	VI	130,000	21	L	25
Primula sinensis	Primula	VIII	18,000	21	D	25
Reseda odorata	Mignonette	I	27,000	21	DL	5
Rosmarinus officinalis	Rosemary	IV	30,000	16	DL	15
Rudbeckia laciniata	Rudbeckia	III	40,000	21	DL	20
Saintpaulia ionantha	Saintpaulia	V	750,000	21	L	25
Salpiglossis sinuata	Salpiglossis	III	125,000	21	D	15
Salvia officinalis	Sage	VIII	3,250	21	D	15
Salvia splendens	Salvia	VI	7,500	21	L	15
Satureia hortensis	Savory	VI	15	18	L	15
Scabiosa atropurpurea	Scabiosa	III	4,500	21	DL	10
Schizanthus pinnatus	Schizanthus	VIII	60,000	16	D	20
Senecio cineraria	Cineraria	VII	65,000	24	L	10
Senecio cruentus	Cineraria	III	150,000	21	DL	10

SPECIES	COMMON NAME	Group[1]	Approximate number seeds per oz	Optimum temperature for best germination (°C)	Continuous light or dark[2]	Usual time required for uniform germination (days)
Sinningia speciosa	Gloxinia	V	800,000	18	L	15
Smithiantha x hybrida	Naegelia	V	1,500,000	21	L	15
Solanum pseudocapsicum	Christmas Cherry	III	12,000	21	DL	20
Streptocarpus x hybridus	Streptocarpus	V	750,000	21	L	15
Tithonia rotundifolia	Tithonia	VIII	3,500	21	D	20
Tagetes erecta	Marigold	I	10,000	21	DL	5
Tagetes patula	Marigold	I	9,000	21	DL	5
Thunbergia gibsonii	Thunbergia	III	500	21	L	10
Thymus vulgaris	Thyme	IV	96,000	24	DL	10
Torenia fournieri	Torenia	III	375,000	21	DL	15
Trachymene caerulea	Didiscus	IV	10,000	18	D	15
Trifolium dubium	Shamrock	IX	28,000	18	D	10
Tropaeolum majus	Nasturtium	IV	175	18	D	8
Valeriana officinalis	Heliotrope	IV	50,000	21	DL	25
Verbena hybrida	Verbena	VIII	10,000	18	D	20
Vinca rosea	Periwinkle	VIII	21,000	21	D	15
Viola cornuta	Viola	IX	24,000	18	D	10
Viola tricolor var. hortensis	Pansy	IX	20,000	18	D	D
Zinnia elegans	Zinnia	III	2,500	21	DL	5

[1] Group Code:

  I - germination over a wide temperature range without a light requirement
  II - germination only at cool temperatures without a light requirement
  III - germination only at warm temperatures without a light requirement
  IV - germination only at a restricted range of temperatures without a light requirement
  V - germination over a wide temperature range when exposed to light
  VI - germination enhanced over a wide temperature range when exposed to light
  VII - germination over a wide temperature range and enhanced at warm temperatures when exposed to light
  VIII - germination over a wide temperature range when held in the dark
  IX - germination over a wide temperature range and enhanced at warm temperatures when held in the dark

[2] L = Requires exposure to continuous light during the germination process; DL = The presence or absence of light during the germination process has no effect; D = Requires exposure to continuous dark during the germination process.

APPENDIX VII — GUIDELINES FOR THE GERMINATION OF VEGETABLE SEEDS

SPECIES	COMMON NAME	Approximate number seeds per oz	Optimum temperature for best germination (°C)	Temperature tolerance or requirement[1]	Continuous light	Usual time required for uniform germination (days)
Allium cepa	Onion	9,500	20	RC	-	6-10
Allium fistulosum	Welsh Onion	-	20	RC	-	6-12
Allium porrum	Leek	11,000	20	RC	-	6-14
Apium graveolens var. dulce	Celery	72,000	10-20	RC	L	10-21
Apium graveolens var. rapaceum	Celeriac	72,000	10-20	RC	-	10-21
Asparagus officinalis	Asparagus	700	20-30	TC	-	7-21
Beta vulgaris	Beet	1,600	20-30	TC	-	3-14
Beta vulgaris var. cicla .	Swiss Chard	1,600	20-30	TC	-	3-14
Brassica chinensis	Pak-choi	18,000	20-30	TC	-	3-7
Brassica juncea	Mustard	18,000	20-30	TC	L	3-7
Brassica napus var. napobrassica	Rutabaga	12,000	20-30	TC	-	3-14
Brassica oleracea var. acephala	Collards, Kale	9,000	20-30	TC	-	3-10
Brassica oleracea var. alboglabra	Chinese Kale	9,000	20-30	TC	-	3-10
Brassica oleracea var. botrytis	Cauliflower	9,000	20-30	TC	-	3-10
Brassica oleracea var. capitata	Cabbage	9,000	20-30	TC	-	3-10
Brassica oleracea var. gemmifera	Brussel Sprouts	9,000	20-30	TC	-	3-10
Brassica oleracea var. gongylodes	Kohlrabi	9,000	20-30	TC	-	3-10
Brassica oleracea var. italica	Broccoli	9,000	20-30	TC	-	3-10
Brassica pekinensis	Chinese Cabbage	18,000	20-30	TC	-	3-7
Brassica perviridis	Spinach Mustard	15,000	20-30	TC	-	3-7
Brassica rapa	Turnip	15,000	20-30	TC	-	3-7
Capsicum spp.	Pepper	4,500	20-30	RW	-	6-14
Cichorium endivia	Endive	27,000	20-30	TC	L	5-14
Cichorium intybus	Chicory	27,000	20-30	TC	L	5-14
Citrullus vulgaris	Citron	300	20-30	RW	-	7-14
Citrullus vulgaris	Watermelon	200-300	20-30	RW	-	4-14
Cucumis melo	Muskmelon (including Cantaloupe)	1,300	20-30	RW	-	4-10
Cucumis sativus	Cucumber	1,100	20-30	RW	-	3-7
Cucurbita moschata and C. maxima	Squash	200-400	20-30	RW	-	4-7

SPECIES	COMMON NAME	Approximate number seeds per oz	Optimum temperature for best germination (°C)	Temperature tolerance or requirement[1]	Continuous light	Usual time required for uniform germination (days)
Cucurbita pepo	Pumpkin	100-300	20-30	RW	-	4-7
Cynara cardunculus	Cardoon	700	20-30	TC	-	7-21
Cynara scolymus	Globe Artichoke	700	20-30	TC	-	7-21
Daucus carota	Carrot	23,000	20-30	TC	-	6-21
Glycine max	Soybean	175-350	20-30	RW	-	5-8
Hibiscus esculentus	Okra	500	20-30	RW	L	4-14
Ipomoea batatas	Sweet Potato	-	25	-	L	-
Lactuca sativa	Lettuce	25,000	20	RC	L	7
Lepidium sativum	Garden Cress	12,000	20	RW	L	4-10
Lycopersicon esculentum	Tomato	11,500	20-30	RW	-	5-14
Pastinaca sativa	Parsnip	12,000	20-30	TC	-	6-28
Petroselinum hortense (P. crispum)	Parsley	18,500	20-30	TC	-	11-28
Phaseolus coccineus	Runner Bean	25-30	20-30	RW	-	5-9
Phaseolus vulgaris	Dry Edible and Garden Beans	100-125	20-30	RW	-	5-8
Phaseolus lunatus	Lima Bean	25-75	20-30	RW	-	5-9
Physalis pubescens	Husk Tomato	35,000	20-30	RW	L	7-28
Pisum sativum	Pea	90-175	20	RC	-	5-8
Raphanus sativus	Radish	2,000-4,000	20	RC	-	4-6
Rheum rhaponticum	Rhubarb	1,700	20-30	TC	L	7-21
Rorippa nasturtium-aquaticum	Water Cress	150,000	20-30	TC	L	4-14
Rumex acetosa	Sorrel	30,000	20-30	TC	L	3-14
Solanum melongena	Eggplant	6,500	20-30	RW	L	7-14
Solanum tuberosum	Potato	-	20	TC	L	-
Spinacea oleracea	Spinach	2,800	15	RC	-	7-21
Taraxacum officinale	Dandelion	35,000	20-30	TC	L	7-21
Tetragonia expansa	New Zealand Spinach	350	10-30	-	-	5-28
Tragopogon porrifolius	Salsify	1,900	20	RC	-	5-10
Valerianella locusta var. olitoria	Cornsalad (Fetticus)	-	20	TC	-	7-28
Vicia faba	Broadbean	20-50	20-30	TC	-	4-14
Vigna sesquipedalis	Asparagus bean	225	20-30	RW	-	5-8
Vigna sinensis	Cowpea (Southern Pea)	225	20-30	RW	-	5-8
Zea mays var. rugosa	Sweet Corn	120-180	20-30	RW	-	4-7

[1] RC = Requires a cool germination environment; TC = Tolerance to a cool germination environment; RW = Requires a warm germination environment.

APPENDIX VIII – SCARIFICATION AND STRATIFICATION REQUIREMENTS FOR SELECTED WOODY ORNAMENTALS

SPECIES	COMMON NAME	STRATIFICATION WARM PERIOD TEMP.°C	DURATION (DAYS)	COLD PERIOD TEMP.°C	DURATION (DAYS)	NOTES
Abies balsamea	Balsam Fir			5	60-90	A longer period may be required.
Abies concolor	White Fir			1-5	40-60	
Abies fraseri	Fraser Fir			5	40+	
Abies homolepsis	Nikko Fir			1-5	30-60	
Abies nordmanniana	Nordmann Fir			1-5	50-70	
Abies procera	Noble Fir			1-5	28-45	
Abies veitchii	Veitch Fir					
Acer campestre	Hedge Maple	20-30	30	2-4	90-180	
Acer ginnala	Amur Maple	20-30	30-60	5	90-150	
Acer negundo	Boxelder			5	60-90	
Acer pennsylvanicum	Striped Maple			5	90-120	
Acer platanoides	Norway Maple			5	90-120	
Acer pseudoplatanus	Planetree Maple			5	90+	
Acer rubrum	Red Maple			5	60-75	Soak in cold H_2O for 5 days prior to treatment.
Acer saccharinum	Silver Maple					No pregermination treatment required.
Acer saccharum	Sugar Maple			2-4	60-90	
Aesculus glabra	Ohio Buckeye			5	90+	
Aesculus hippocastanum	Horsechestnut			5	90+	
Ailanthus altissima	Tree of Heaven			5	60	Soaking in water for 10 days may aid germination.
Albizia julibrissin	Mimosa					Brief H_2SO_4 or mechanical treatment to overcome impermeable seed coat.
Amelanchier alnifolia	Service Berry, Juneberry, Shadblow			2-4	180	Treatment with H_2SO_4 may be helpful.
Aronia arbutifolia	Red Chokeberry			1-5	90	
Aronia melanocarpa	Black Chokeberry			5	90	
Aronia prunifolia	Purple Chokeberry			1-10	60	

| | | STRATIFICATION | | | | |
| | | WARM PERIOD | | COLD PERIOD | | |
SPECIES	COMMON NAME	TEMP. °C	DURATION (DAYS)	TEMP. °C	DURATION (DAYS)	NOTES
Asimina triloba	Papaw			5	100	
Berberis thunbergi	Japanese Barberry			1-5	15-40	
Betula nigra	River Birch			5	30-60	
Betula papyrifera	Paper Birch			5	60-75	
Betula pendula	European White Birch			1-10	30-60	
Carpinus caroliniana	Hornbeam			2-7	100-120	
Carya glabra	Pignut			1-7	90-120	Less if seed dry stored for 1 year.
Carya illinoensis	Pecan			1-7	30-90	
Carya ovata	Shagbark Hickory			1-7	90-150	30-60 days may be sufficient if dry stored for 1 or more years.
Carya tomentosa	Mockernut			1-2	90-105	
Castanea dentata	American Chestnut			0-5	?	Duration unknown.
Castanea mollissima	Chinese Chestnut			0-5	?	Duration unknown.
Catalpa bignonioides	Catalpa					No treatment necessary.
Cedrus atlantica	Atlas Cedar			3-5	14	Seeds of all Cedrus are oily and do not keep well.
Cedrus deodora	Deodora Cedar			3-5	14	All Cedrus seeds exhibit little or no dormancy.
Cedrus libani	Cedar of Lebanon			3-5	14	
Celtis occidentalis	Hackberry			5	60-90	
Cercis canadensis	Eastern Redbud			5	60-90	Treatment with 1/2-1 hr of H_2SO_4 prior to cold treatment.
Chamaecyparis lawsoniana	Lawson False Cypress	20-30	30	5	30	
Chamaecyparis thyoides	White Cedar	20-30	30	5	30	
Chionanthus virginicus	Fringetree	20	30-90	5	30+	
Cladrastis lutea	Yellowwood			5	90	Scarification with H_2SO_4 for 30-60 min may substitute for cold treatment.
Cornus alba	Tatarian Dogwood			5	60	
Cornus alternifolia	Blue Dogwood	20-30	60	1	120-150	
Cornus canadensis	Bunchberry	25	30-60	5	120	
Cornus florida	Dogwood			1-5	40-120	
Cornus kousa	Japanese Dogwood	20-30	120	1-12	30-120	
Cornus mas	Cornelian Cherry	20-30	60	5	60	
Cornus racemosa	Gray Dogwood					

SPECIES	COMMON NAME	WARM PERIOD TEMP.°C	WARM PERIOD DURATION (DAYS)	COLD PERIOD TEMP.°C	COLD PERIOD DURATION (DAYS)	NOTES
Cornus sericea	Red-Osier Dogwood			5	60-90	
Cotinus coggygria	Smoketree			4	60-80	
Cotoneaster apiculata	Cranberry Cotoneaster			5	90	
Cotoneaster horizontalis	Rock Cotoneaster			5	90-120	
Crataegus arnoldiana	Arnold Hawthorn			2-9	180	Pretreat in H_2SO_4 for 2 hrs.
Crataegus crus-galli	Cockspur Thorn	21-25	21	1	21-135	Pretreat in H_2SO_4 for 2-3 hrs.
Crataegus mollis	Downy Hawthorn	30	21	10	180	Pretreat in H_2SO_4 for 4-5 hrs.
Crataegus phaenopyrum	Washington Hawthorn			5-10	135	Pretreat in H_2SO_4 for 2-3 hrs.
Cryptomeria japonica	Cryptomeria			1	60-90	
Cytisus scoparius	Scotch Broom	20-30	28			Pretreat with hot H_2O or H_2SO_4 recommended.
Diospyros virginiana	Persimmon			2-10	60-90	Pretreat with H_2SO_4 for 1-2 hrs may be helpful.
Elaeagnus angustifolia	Russian Olive			1-10	10-90	Pretreat with H_2SO_4 for 1/2-1 hr helpful.
Elaeagnus umbellata	Autumn Elaeagnus			1-10	10-90	
Euonymus alatus	Winged Euonymus			1-10	90-100	
Fagus grandifolia	American Beech			5	90	
Fagus sylvatica	European Beech			5	90	
Fraxinus americana	White Ash	20-30	30	5	60	
Fraxinus excelsior	European Ash	20	60-90	5	60-90	
Fraxinus ornus	Flowering Ash	20	30	5	90	
Fraxinus pennsylvanica	Green Ash			1-5	60-210	
Ginkgo biloba	Ginkgo					
Gleditsia triacanthos	Honeylocust					Treat with H_2SO_4 for 1-2 hrs.
Gymnocladus dioicus	Kentucky Coffeetree					H_2SO_4 treat for 2 hrs.
Halesia carolina	Carolina Silverbell	12-30	60-120	1-5	60-90	
Hamamelis virginiana	Witch-Hazel	30	60	5	90	
Ilex aquifolium	English Holly					Ilex seeds require up to 3 years in nature to complete germination.
Ilex glabra	Inkberry					
Ilex opaca	American Holly	20-30	60	5	60	
Ilex verticillata	Winterberry					
Ilex vomitoria	Yaupon					
Juglans nigra	Black Walnut			1-5	90-120	
Juniperus communis	Common Juniper	20-30	60-90	5	90+	
Juniperus virginiana	Redcedar			5	30-120	

313

SPECIES	COMMON NAME	STRATIFICATION				NOTES
		WARM PERIOD		COLD PERIOD		
		TEMP.°C	DURATION (DAYS)	TEMP.°C	DURATION (DAYS)	
Kalmia latifolia	Mountain Laurel					Require light for germination.
Koelreuteria paniculata	Golden Rain Tree			5	90	Treat with H_2SO_4 for 1-2 hrs.
Larix decidua	European Larch			5	60	
Larix laricina	American Larch			5	60	
Libocedrus decurrens	Incense-Cedar			3-5	30-60	
Ligustrum amurense	Amur Privet					Will germinate without pre- treatment - immediately after harvest.
Ligustrum japonicum	Japanese Privet					
Ligustrum lucidum	Glossy Privet					
Ligustrum vulgare	European Privet			0-3	60-90	
Liquidambar styraciflua	Sweetgum			1	15-90	
Liriodendron tulipifera	Yellow Poplar			1	60-90	
Lonicera maackii	Amur Honeysuckle			0-10	60-90	
Lonicera tatarica	Tatarian Honeysuckle			5	30-60	
Maclura pomifera	Osage Orange			5	30	Also overcome by 48 hrs soak in water.
Magnolia acuminata	Cucumbertree			1-5	90-180	
Magnolia grandiflora	Southern Magnolia			1-5	90-180	
Magnolia virginiana	Sweetbay Magnolia			1-5	90-180	
Malus baccata	Siberian Crab			5	30	
Malus coronaria	Sweet Crab			5	120	
Malus floribunda	Japanese Crab			5	60-120	
Malus ioensis	Prairie Crab			5	60	
Metasequoia glyptostroboides	Dawn Redwood					Will germinate without pretreat- ment.
Morus alba	Mulberry			1-5	30-90	
Myrica pensylvanica	Bayberry			1-5	60-90	
Nyssa sylvatica	Sour-gum			5	30	
Ostrya virginiana	Hophornbeam	20-30	60	5	140	
Oxydendron arboreum	Sourwood			5	60	
Parthenocissus quinquefolia	Virginia Creeper			5	60	
Paulownia tomentosa	Empress Tree					
Phellodendron amurense	Amur Corktree					
Picea abies	Norway Spruce					No dormancy; germinate immediately.
Picea engelmannii	Engelmann Spruce					No dormancy; germinate immediately.
Picea glauca	White Spruce			5	60-90	No dormancy; germinate immediately.
Picea omorika	Serbian Spruce					No dormancy; germinate immediately.
Picea orientalis	Oriental Spruce					
Picea polita	Tigertail Spruce					

| | | STRATIFICATION | | | | |
| | | WARM PERIOD | | COLD PERIOD | | |
SPECIES	COMMON NAME	TEMP.°C	DURATION (DAYS)	TEMP.°C	DURATION (DAYS)	NOTES
Picea pungens	Blue Spruce			5	14-90	May germinate without treatment.
Picea sitchensis	Sitka Spruce					
Pinus cembra	Swiss Stone Pine			1-5	90-270	Pretreat 3-5 hrs in H_2SO_4.
Pinus densiflora	Japanese Red Pine					May germinate without treatment.
Pinus echinata	Shortleaf Pine			1-5	0-15	May germinate without treatment.
Pinus mugo	Swiss Mountain Pine					May germinate without treatment.
Pinus nigra	Austrian Pine					May germinate without treatment.
Pinus palustris	Longleaf Pine					
Pinus parviflora	Japanese White Pine			1-5	90	
Pinus strobus	White Pine			1-5	60	
Pinus sylvestris	Scotch Pine					May germinate without treatment.
Pinus taeda	Loblolly Pine			1-5	30-60	
Pinus thunbergii	Japanese Black Pine					May germinate without treatment.
Pinus virginiana	Scrub Pine			1-5	0-30	
Platanus occidentalis	Sycamore					No pregermination treatment required.
Platanus orientalis	Oriental Planetree					
Populus deltoides	Cottonwood					No dormancy.
Populus tremuloides	Quaking Aspen					No dormancy.
Prunus amygdalus	Almond			1-5	65	
Prunus armeniaca	Apricot			1-5	180	
Prunus avium	Mazzard Cherry			1-5	90-180	
Prunus besseyi	Western Sand Cherry			1-5	120	
Prunus cerasifera	Myrobalan Plum	20-30	14	1-5	180	
Prunus cerasus	Sour Cherry			1-5	90-150	
Prunus domestica	Plum	20-30	14	1-5	180	
Prunus persica	Peach			1-5	70-105	
Prunus pumila	Sand Cherry	20-30	60	1-5	120	
Prunus serotina	Black Cherry	20-30	14	1-5	120	
Prunus virginiana	Chokecherry			1-5	120-160	
Pseudotsuga menziesii	Douglas Fir			1-5	20-40	
Pyrus communis	Pear			1-7	60-90	
Quercus alba (W)	White Oak				0	With few exceptions acorns of White Oak group have little or no dormancy and will germinate immediately after falling.
Quercus bicolor (W)	Swamp White Oak				0	
Quercus coccinea (B)	Scarlet Oak			1-5	30-60	
Quercus falcata (B)	Southern Red Oak			1-5	30-90	

| | | STRATIFICATION | | | | |
| | | WARM PERIOD | | COLD PERIOD | | |
SPECIES	COMMON NAME	TEMP.°C	DURATION (DAYS)	TEMP.°C	DURATION (DAYS)	NOTES
Quercus imbricaria (B)	Shingle Oak			1-5	30-60	Acorns of Black Oak group exhibit embryo dormancy.
Quercus macrocarpa (W)	Bur Oak			1-5	30-60	(W) = White Oak Group
Quercus mühlenbergii (W)	Chinkapin Oak				0	(B) = Black Oak Group
Quercus nigra (B)	Water Oak			1-5	30-60	
Quercus palustris (B)	Pin Oak			1-5	30-60	
Quercus phellos (B)	Willow Oak			1-5	30-60	
Quercus robur (W)	English Oak				0	
Quercus rubra (B)	Northern Red Oak			1-5	30-45	
Quercus shumardii (B)	Shumard Oak			1-5	60-120	
Quercus velutina (B)	Black Oak			1-5	30-60	
Quercus virginiana (W)	Live Oak				0	
Rhamnus frangula	Buckthorn			1-5	60	
Rhododendron catawbiense	Rosebay					No pretreatment required.
Rhododendron maximum	Rhododendron					Seeds must have light to germinate.
Ribes alpinum	Alpine Currant			1-10	90	
Robina pseudoacacia	Black Locust					10-20 min of H_2SO_4.
Rosa canina	Dog Rose	24	60-90	1-5	150	
Rosa multiflora	Multiflora Rose			1-5	120	
Rosa rugosa	Rugosa Rose			1-5	90-120	
Salix discolor	Pussy Willow					No dormancy.
Salix nigra						No dormancy.
Sambucus canadensis	Common Elder	20-30	60	5	90-150	
Sassafras albidum	Sassafras			5	120	
Sciadopitys verticillata	Umbrella Pine	16-21	100	1-10	90	
Sorbus americana	American Mountain Ash			1-5	150	
Sorbus aucuparia	European Mountain Ash			1-5	60-120	
Symphoricarpos orbiculatus	Coralberry	21	210	5	180	30 min pretreat in H_2SO_4.
Syringa amurensis	Amur Lilac			5	30-60	Not always necessary - depends upon seed list.
Syringa persica	Persian Lilac					
Syringa vulgaris	Common Lilac					
Taxodium distichum	Bald Cypress			5	90	Preceeded by 5 min soak in Ethyl alcohol helpful.
Taxus baccata	English Yew	16	120	2-5	365	
Taxus canadensis	Canadian Yew			2-5	365	
Taxus cuspidata	Japanese Yew	16	120	2-5	365	

SPECIES	COMMON NAME	WARM PERIOD TEMP.°C	DURATION (DAYS)	COLD PERIOD TEMP.°C	DURATION (DAYS)	NOTES
Thuja occidentalis	American Arborvitae					Occasionally dormant seed lots are encountered.
Thuja orientalis	Oriental Arborvitae					Pretreat with H_2SO_4 30-60 min.
Tilia americana	American Linden			1-4	90	
Tilia cordata	Littleleaf Linden					
Tsuga canadensis	Canadian Hemlock			1-5	30-120	
Tsuga caroliniana	Carolina Hemlock			3-5	30-90	
Ulmus americana	American Elm					No dormancy.
Ulmus parvifolia	Chinese Elm			5	30-60	
Ulmus pumila	Siberian Elm					No dormancy.
Viburnum acerifolium	Mapleleaf Viburnum	20-30	180-500	1-5	60-120	
Viburnum cassinoides	Witherod	20-30	60	1-5	90	
Viburnum dentatum	Southern Arrowwood					No dormancy.
Viburnum lantana	Wayfaringtree			1-5	70	
Viburnum lentago	Nannyberry	20-30	150-270	1-5	60-120	
Viburnum opulus	Cranberrybush	20-30	60-90	1-5	30-60	
Viburnum prunifolium	Blackhaw	20-30	150-270	1-5	30-60	
Vitex agnus-castus	Vitex			5	90	